# MARSHALL ISLANDS

# LEGENDS
## AND
# STORIES

told by
Tonke Aisea, Koju Alfred, Josapeth Amram, Jorju Arre, Neilem
Baneb, Kiat Benjamin, Iban Edwin, Bolden Elbon, Jia Hisaiah,
Jackning Jajōñ, Nitwa Jeik, Jeljel Jerbal, Hecekeia Jibba, Mejin Jitiam,
Rose Johnson, Lene Langbol, McKay Langmouir, Lakilmej Line

collected and edited by
Daniel A. Kelin II

Illustrated by Nashton T. Nashon

3565 Harding Avenue
Honolulu, Hawai'i 96816
phone: (808) 734-7159
fax: (808) 732-3627
e-mail: sales@besspress.com
http://www.besspress.com

Design: Carol Colbath

Library of Congress Cataloging-in-Publication Data

  Marshall Islands legends and
stories / told by Tonke Aisea ...
[et al.] ; collected and edited by
Daniel A. Kelin II ; illustrated
by Nashton T. Nashon.
        p.          cm.
  Includes illustrations, glossary.
  ISBN 1-57306-141-7 (hardcover)
  ISBN 1-57306-140-9 (paperback)
  1. Legends - Marshall Islands.
2. Tales - Marshall Islands.
I. Kelin II, Daniel A.  II. Nashon,
Nashton T., ill.  III. Title.
GR385.M37.K45 2003   398.2099683-dc21

03  04  05  06  07  08      6  5  4  3  2  1

Iban Edwin, "Ellice Island Rimenanuwe," recorded and
translated by Daniel A. Kelin II, reprinted from *Marvels
& Tales: Journal of Fairy-Tale Studies,* Vol. 13, No. 2
(1999), pp. 234–237. Copyright © 1999 by Wayne State
University Press, Detroit, MI 48201.

Jia Hisaiah and Iban Edwin, "Reef Eyes," recorded and
translated by Daniel A. Kelin II, reprinted from
*Highlights for Children,* Vol. 57, No. 4 (April 2002), pp.
11-13. Copyright © 2002 by Highlights for Children, Inc.

Printed in the United States of America

Yokwe,

We are pleased to share legends from Lolelaplap, the traditional name of the Marshall Islands.

Enjoy these legends as told by storytellers from many atolls. We invite you to meet our people and visit our country.


Kemij monono in kwalok inon kein am jen Lolelaplap, at eo etan ailin kein am etto.

Kemij kejatdikdik bwe kom naj monono in riti inon kein jen ri-komman bwebwenato ro jen ailin kein am.

Kemji borainwot monono in karuwainene kom ilo ami naj itok im ione armej in Majol im lotok ailin kein am.

Iroij Manini Mike Kabua

# CONTENTS

# PREFACE AND ACKNOWLEDGMENTS

This collection is a labor of love. I loved sitting and listening to each and every one of these stories. I loved visiting the various islands the storytellers live on, staying in local homes or sleeping at the schoolhouse or local hospital. I loved being welcomed into the homes of the storytellers, or welcoming them into mine, sharing food and legends, laughter and respect. I loved sitting in small lantern-lit homes on quiet islands, with the sound of the ocean in the background and people scattered about, half-working, half-listening to the legends. This collection is a sign of my respect for the trust the storytellers placed in me by sharing their stories and a way of sharing with readers my love of the islands, their people, and their stories.

*"Iakwe"* has been the storytellers' way to welcome me to their islands, into their houses, and into their hearts. I've been lucky to be welcomed many times to the Marshall Islands. The storytellers have been very generous toward me. People on both **Namdrik** and **Mili** "adopted" me. The men of **Maloelap** gave me tours and plenty of friendship. They shared snails, fish, breadfruit, bananas, chickens, pigs, and coconuts with me. Occasionally I stayed in their homes. I sang with them, danced for them, talked story about America and the rest of the world with them, and a couple of times gave them rides to other islands. The planes and boats I rode home in were often filled with presents of food.

It is not customary for storytellers in the Marshall Islands to share legends with just anyone. By custom the *iroij* own the legends, and the ones who are chosen to remember them can share them

*iakwe*
[ee-ah-KWEH]
literally, "You are the rainbow"; greetings, love

**Namdrik**
NAHM-rihk

**Mili** MIH-leh

**Maloelap**
mah-LOH-eh-lap

*iroij* [ih-ROHJ]
chief

only when the *iroij* says so. I was a lucky one. In all cases, I or someone I was working or staying with obtained permission for me to listen to and use the stories in this collection. Not everyone was willing to share legends, but for the most part the many chiefs, health assistants, mayors, storytellers, members of local church groups and youth groups and other people who lived on the islands I visited were cooperative, supportive, and gracious about sharing with me. The storytellers were happy that a collection of legends would not only preserve their tales, but also pass them on to future generations.

I don't profess to be an anthropologist, ethnologist, or folklorist. As a storyteller and drama educator, I believe that legends and stories told aloud are far different from legends on paper. They are living entities. They provide engaging ways of sharing the uniqueness of culture, place, and beliefs. That is why I use folk stories as a significant part of my work. When I do so, I am either sharing stories with an audience in an improvisational manner or having my students explore them in that same way. To be truly effective, the printed stories need to retain this sense of "aliveness" and "uniqueness." Putting the tales down on paper certainly doesn't capture the experience of hearing them to the background music of the ocean, under an open night sky or with the flicker of a lamp playing shadows on the walls. However, I have tried to convey some of the qualities of those experiences.

Editing and adapting were necessary parts of the process of recording these legends on paper and making sure they reflect the culture of the island each came from and the specific storyteller who told them. I have tried to capture the storytellers' unique styles. Many of the storytellers offered comments before, during, and after the legends, and I have retained many of those. Many Marshallese storytellers repeat words to indicate the passage of time or the extremity of an event. I have retained repetitions as well. I have edited the legends only to clarify the action and characters or to fill out the narrative. In other words, the legends as they appear in this book represent my attempt to preserve the unique styles of oral tellings in an easily read and understood printed form. Any mistakes are mine and mine alone.

I first visited the Marshall Islands in 1991 to work with an organization dedicated to teaching youth about health, social, and cultural issues. I have returned nearly every year since, primarily during the summers, for up to nine weeks at a time. With each successive trip, I came to admire the people and the culture more. As a part of my work with youth, I began to draw on the folklore of the Marshall Islands to create small drama presentations that the youth performed in the islands. At the same time, the Honolulu Theatre for Youth commissioned me to write a play based on the folklore of the Marshall Islands.

In 1993, shortly after receiving the commission, I took my first summer trip to Majuro to work with Marshallese youth. Within days of my arrival, Darlene Keju-Johnson took me on a side trip to **Wotje** Atoll. Can one be any luckier than to spend the night in the house of the very storyteller one is supposed to meet?

Wotje WOHT-je

A few months later I took my first jaunt to Namdrik Atoll, my first "official" trip to the Marshall Islands to collect legends for my play. I say "official" because I had recently been awarded a Rockefeller Foundation grant to support my work with storytellers from that island. I flew to Namdrik specifically to meet with two renowned choreographers/songmasters/storytellers, men who had represented the Marshall Islands at the 1992 South Pacific Arts Festival. When I arrived, a gentleman approached me and guided me to meet Jia and Iban—"the two old men" he called them. Jia wore a t-shirt and baseball cap, and Iban wore a crooked pair of sunglasses and no shoes and had one pant leg rolled up—he'd been fishing. They considered me a special guest; both Jia and Iban picked up my bags to escort me to my lodgings.

A translator and I met with Jia and Iban for several nights, listening to and recording legends. At our first session, Jia told just a very short, and seemingly incomplete, legend. I asked Iban if there was more to this particular legend. He told me he could not tell the rest of the legend. By custom, the storytellers of the island are not supposed to share that particular legend with outsiders. So that was that. He never said more about it, and I never encountered that particular restriction again. During the rest of our sessions, legends flowed freely.

I returned the following summer to spend another week with my storytelling partners in Namdrik. This trip was marked by a great deal of **bwebwenato**, a word that means both "story" and "conversation." We talked to pass the time (Jia and Iban rarely showed up at the same time), but also out of cultural respect. Giving and sharing are important in Marshallese culture. Jia and Iban would bring food over, I would have tea ready, and then we would sit on the cement floor of my temporary home to eat and drink tea and talk about their experiences during the Japanese occupation or about Mars or the death of Jacqueline Kennedy.

**bwebwenato**
[bway-bway-NAH-doh]
story, conversation; stories believed to be true

**Letao**, the trickster figure of the Marshall Islands, often slipped into a story with little warning. Before one evening's sharing, Iban and I sat drinking tea and waiting for Jia. In the midst of a quiet moment of sipping, Iban announced that Jia was going to show us a dance about Letao. In Iban's easy manner of *bwebwenato* he spontaneously began to tell the legend that accompanies the dance, and my translator had to jump in quickly to catch up. I didn't have my recorder on, didn't have my notebook out, but did have my interest up, so I sat, enjoying myself, as Iban detailed the short tale. When Jia and his dancers arrived, their performance was even more humorous than the legend. Jia liked it so much he had the dancers repeat it.

Letao LEH-dow

Each year I visited a new island and new storytellers. Occasionally people were resistant, but I was never able to find out why. A couple of times the resistance was vehement, though never hostile. As I learned in my sessions with Iban, telling some legends to outsiders goes against custom. In one particular case a woman said she wouldn't share legends because she was afraid that the *iroij* would be angry with her. One evening I had dinner with her and she told a legend. I couldn't record it and I can't tell it.

I've met with navigators, fishermen, storytellers, dancers, church officials—a whole range of the population. Although a few of the stories have shared a basic structure or story line or characters, most have been unique to a specific place and island.

Most, also, have been preserved because of the interest of a few people. Although a couple of the people whose stories I recorded are deemed the storytellers of their island or atoll, many were never officially "chosen." They learned the legends because they listened to the legends. They had the interest and the wherewithal to sit and listen to their parents or grandparents or to visit the old people of their island. Many told me that their own siblings didn't seem interested so they themselves became the person in their family, or on their island, to remember the legends.

I learned that not too long ago, maybe a couple of generations, legends were regularly shared, mostly in the evenings. There were a few rules. The storytellers would stop telling if people wandered by, as if the audience was a chosen one. This rule wasn't universal; others told stories whenever a group of people was around. One storyteller told of hanging around older people just so he could hear the legends the older people swapped.

The tellers were excited by my interest in the legends, and also by the idea of sharing food, ideas, company, and occasionally songs and dances. Some were happy that the legends would be shared with both Marshallese children (who, most bemoaned, were uninterested nowadays) and American children. Some were relieved that the legends were being preserved, since their children and other relatives had expressed no interest in hearing the legends. In one case people heard a storyteller's tales for the first time because they wanted to know what had made me so interested in spending time on their island.

**dri-bwebwenato**
[ree-bway-bway-NAH-doh]
storyteller

It's now been over ten years since I first sat down with a **dri-bwebwenato**. But I'm not done. I've promised to return to a couple of the islands and listen to more legends from Jackning and Kiat and Nitwa and others. They've promised to take me to more of the islands on their boats and have me stay with them and share some meals. I don't think I'll be completely happy until I know I've talked with every person in the Marshall Islands who would like to share a legend.

This collection exists because of the tellers. It is for them. I feel honored to have been given their legends and I hope this small collection (about half of the legends I've been given) does honor to them. I offer my thanks

To those who started it, Darlene Keju-Johnson, Alfred Capelle, and Andrew Hisaiah.

To the first two tellers, Iban Edwin and Jia Hisaiah.

To the staff at JNJIE, especially Marita Edwin, Sylvia Lolin, and Hespy John.

To a good friend, Ben Benjamin.

To the health assistants who put me up and fed me on the many islands.

To the many *iroij* who gave me permission to collect the stories.

To the church youth groups, women's groups, and families who took care of me, celebrated my presence on their islands, and gave me lots of food.

To those who helped me translate and understand: Darlene, Sylvia, Hespy, Ben, Ranny, Keyko Samuel, Ajeluk Beaja, Omita Jorlang, Hilda Heine, and Charity Joel.

Most especially to the tellers themselves for letting a stranger with a few gifts listen to the stories and be trusted to share them with others.

Now we share the legends with you. Tell one or two of them. It will certainly make Jorju happy. It will infuse the legends with the life they deserve. **Kommol tata**.

*kommol tata*
[KOHM-mohl DAH-dah] thank you very much

# INTRODUCTION

## The Marshall Islands

The Marshall Islands are located in the Pacific Ocean just north of the equator and a bit west of the International Date Line. Spread over 750,000 square miles of water are twenty-nine atolls and five islands consisting of more than twelve hundred separate islets (the exact number depending on the height of the tide). Many islands are no more than seven feet above sea level; the highest point is about thirty feet. Some islands are as long as ten miles (**Majuro**, at thirty miles, was artificially constructed), but rarely more than four hundred yards wide. The lagoons range from less than a mile to thirty miles across and as much as seventy-five miles long. The atolls and islands make up two almost parallel chains known as the **Ratak** (Sunrise) group and **Ralik** (Sunset) group. The tiny islands look like bits of earth sprinkled across the ocean. Their combined land area, seventy square miles, is less than half that of Rhode Island's.

People first arrived in these tiny islands between about 500 and 2000 B.C., calling the atolls **Aelon Kein Ad** (Our Islands). Archeological finds on Bikini Atoll have been carbon dated to 2000 B.C.

Responsibilities in Marshall Islands society are divided among *iroij* (chiefs), *alap*, and *rijerbal*. The *iroij* control land tenure, resource use and distribution, and dispute settlement. The *alap*'s responsibilities include overseeing the land and supervising daily deeds. The *rijerbal* carry out the daily work: building, fishing, collecting food. Inheritance is matrilineal (passed through the mother).

**Majuro**
MAH-joo-roh

**Ratak**
RAH-dahk

**Ralik** REYE-lihk

**Aelōñ Kein Ad**
eye-LEUHNG
kayn ahr

*alap* [AH-lahp]
clan heads

*rijerbal* [ree-jer-BAHL]
workers

Older ways are evident still on the Outer Islands, but on the capital island of Majuro Western influence and traditional values collide. Only the major islands of each of the atolls have landing strips, so to get to the tiniest islands requires either a motorboat or a small traditional outrigger canoe. Few islanders have vehicles, electricity, or plumbing.

The elements that compose the Marshallese culture and landscape make for interesting stories in and of themselves: the many islands, the people both at odds and strangely comfortable with Western culture; the fragments of Japanese warplanes overcome by the underbrush; abandoned solid-cement copra factories, some now taken over as homes; beaches strewn with a huge mix of water, shells, rocks, and rusty ships—all crowded underneath the multitudinous palm trees.

## The Legends

Studies I've read refer to two major categories of legends in the Marshall Islands: ***inoñ*** and *bwebwenato*. I seldom found those categories used. I have also read that legends traditionally start and end with the following phrases: ***etto im etto, kilin wōt ne***, and ***jidip inoñ, jidim jedu,*** but I haven't encountered tellers who regularly use any of those. I came to like "*etto im etto*" and I have used it whenever I have created a folklore play with Marshallese youth. However, that was my own imposition. The tellers, I believe, used the phrase around me once in a while because they knew I liked it.

Chiefs own the legends, and the storytellers need permission to tell them even to people on their own islands. Perhaps this is because legends are a source of power—a power that sometimes seemed

***inoñ*** [ih-NOHNG] stories not believed to be true

***etto im etto*** [ET-toh ihm ET-toh] "long and long time past"

***kilin wōt ne*** [KIH-lihn weuht neh]

***jidip inoñ, jidim jedu*** [JIH-rihp ih-NOHNG JIH-rihm je-DOO] "That's the end of the story."

uncannily reflected in my own experience. For example, at every legend-based performance my students gave, it rained. For me the rain represents a validation of the work that the youth group, the storytellers, and I were doing. The importance of rain to coral atolls cannot be overstated, and, to my mind, the rain falling each and every time the youth group performed was a symbol hard to ignore. I know the performance and the rain are separate entities, but for me, being regularly soaked in the symbolism of folklore, it was hard not to imagine the rain taking on a greater significance in its consistent appearance at our performances.

Another illustration of legends' power is that many storytellers feel embarrassed by certain legends when they reflect the bad side of their island, its people, or their relatives. They always put the legend into a contemporary context, adding a comment such as "It's true. The women of this island are still lazy." Or, "I feel bad telling you this story because I don't want you to think that all the people here are ugly like that." However, they also say how important it is to remember these things and how they remind the listeners about correct ways to behave.

Folklore, legends, and myths are ways to explain the unexplainable, to celebrate the incredible, and to preserve the uniqueness of culture. A feature of the Letao stories is the oft-used ending (or some variant), "Letao is now in America. That's why the people there are so smart." This ending always causes gales of laughter among Marshallese listeners. It seems to have evolved as a simple and humorous way of dealing with the perceived awesome power of the United States. By claiming that Letao moved from the Marshall Islands to the United States, the

Marshallese take credit for all that power and also justify the supportive/destructive nature of the U.S.'s relationship with the islands.

It seems likely that most of the pre-missionary songs, dances, and folklore don't exist anymore. Dance and other entertainment described by early European writers, such as Otto Von Kotzebue, are different from what exists now. One notable exception is the *jebwa* dance performed on Ujae Atoll. An old Japanese anthropological source describes a dance very much like the *jebwa* dance. As for the legends, if you do enough reading of Pacific tales, you'll see similarities to tales from other cultures, including European ones. (I once heard part of a tale that is most likely an "islandized" Jack and the Beanstalk.)

*jebwa* JEB-wah

These are the stories as told to me by the storytellers. Several of them differ from versions found in other collections, and from those that other storytellers might tell. I avoided "correcting" the stories to match the accepted or "real" version of the story. My intent has always been to capture the story the way the storyteller shared it with me. A good example is the story of **Tobolar** as told to me by Nitwa Jeik. He started the telling by saying, "Do you know the story of Tobolar? Well, that one's wrong. This is how the story goes . . . ," and then proceeded to tell me quite a different version of the story than will be found in other books or told by nearly anyone else.

**Tobolar**
TOH-boh-lahr

## Language and Spelling

The Marshallese language, like all languages, is evolving. The only existing dictionary of the Marshallese language, published almost thirty years ago, is an academic work intended for English speakers. The spellings in this book are those in common use in the Marshalls Islands today, although some readers may be more familiar with variant spellings.

Pronunciations and definitions are provided for key Marshallese names and terms at the first appearance of the name or term in the text. A complete glossary is located at the end of the book.

# RATAK CHAIN *Sunrise Islands*
# AILUK

# AILUK

Ailuk EYE-look

## LENE LANGBOL

Lene Langbol
LAHNG-eh
LANHG-bohl

Lene lives near the old hospital at the end of Ailuk Atoll. He has a beautiful view of both the ocean and the lagoon. I listened to his stories as the sun set over his shoulder.

Like most Marshallese, he traces his family back to a number of different atolls—in his case, **Mejit**, Ailuk, **Likiep**, and Maloelap particularly. His *joui* is **Raur**. His grandfather, **Jobi**, taught him navigation when he was about fourteen years old. He schooled with his grandfather for about four months. The hardest part, Lene told me, was learning to read the waves. His grandfather could watch the water that flooded into the canoe and know which way they were headed.

Lene cannot walk well ("something happened to

Mejit MEH-jeet

Likiep LEE-kee-eb

joui [JOH-wee]
  clan

Raur rah-OOR

Jobi JOH-bee

2

my legs") and pulls himself along on two small mats. During our story sessions we sat on a broken slab of concrete outside his small house. He liked to speak English to make me laugh. As I left one day he called out, "Maybe I'll see you in heaven." Then he added, "Maybe I'll see you in Honolulu. **Nānākuli**!"

As fascinating as his stories are, one particular event in his life I found especially amazing. An **Utrik** chief named **Iroñ** asked the men of Ailuk to take him to **Bikar**. Four boats sailed together on this trip, the biggest of which held eight men, the smallest, five. There were two navigators on the trip, **Mokba** and Jobi, Lene's grandfather. Jobi let Lene take control of the boat a little at a time. They sailed for a day and a night.

On Bikar there lives a small bird, about the size of the end of your finger. Belief has it that if someone kills it, there will be a big storm. When the group landed, one of the men carried his grandson on his shoulders to shore. One of the small birds landed on the boy's head. The boy killed it.

They had planned to be there for only a week, but when the boy killed the bird they decided to build a small house and gather water from a catchment made a long time ago by a chief named **Launbikar**. It's a hole in the ground lined with coral rock.

A big storm hit the island. They waited and slept. Custom dictated they couldn't do much else. It was several weeks before they could leave.

**Nānākuli** [NAH NAH koo lee] a town on the Wai'anae Coast of the island of O'ahu, Hawai'i

**Utrik** OO-trihk

**Iroñ** ee-ROHNG

**Bikar** bee-KAHR

**Mokba** MOHK-bah

**Launbikar** LAWHN-bih-kahr

# LIJEBAKE

**Lijebake**
lee-jeh-BAH-keh

**Kiribati**
[KIH rih bus] an
independent
island group
southeast of the
Marshall Islands

**Wōt Kileplep**
WEUHT kih-
LEP-lep

*I'll start with **Kiribati**, because this story begins there.*

The girl **Wōt Kileplep** (Heavy Rain) lived in Kiribati with her family. When the rain fell, Heavy Rain always forgot the mats and clothes outside. The rain ruined the mats. New clothes had to be made again and again. The family got really angry with Heavy Rain. Sometimes they beat her.

After one heavy rain and more anger, Heavy Rain ran away to the shore and cried. As she cried, a turtle crawled up from the ocean. "What happened?" the turtle asked.

"Grandmother," cried Heavy Rain. "They're so angry because the stuff got all wet."

"Well," said her grandmother the turtle, "you come with me, my little one."

Heavy Rain climbed onto her grandmother's back. She held tight as her grandmother the turtle, Lijebake, swam off from Kiribati.

Lijebake headed north to the islands of her people. Her daughter, Heavy Rain's mother, had married a Kiribati man and stayed there. Lijebake felt it was time to take Heavy Rain to her true home.

When they neared Mili Atoll, in the Ratak chain of the Marshall Islands, Lijebake said, "We should take a rest, Heavy Rain."

Lots of chewed **pandanus** floated about. Many

**pandanus**
fiber made from
the leaves of the
screw pine tree;
it is used in
weaving mats
and other items

4

people stayed at that island. It wouldn't be safe to stop there. Heavy Rain chanted to her grandmother:

> *Wawoj wawoj wot.*
> *Just keep going.*

Heavy Rain kept watch behind her as Lijebake swam on past Mili. She was afraid her family might follow.

**Arno** Atoll appeared at the edge of the sky.

"How about here?" Lijebake asked, as they floated closer. Chewed pandanus surrounded them.

> *Wawoj wawoj wot.*
> *Just keep going.*

Lijebake kept on, hoping the waves might calm Heavy Rain, but knowing they couldn't shake the memory of how her granddaughter had been treated.

They came quickly to Majuro Atoll, at a place called **Litakboki**. Pandanus bobbed all around them. Heavy Rain called out, "Still too many people, grandmother."

> *Wawoj wawoj wot.*
> *Just keep going.*

Lijebake understood her granddaughter's fear but knew they needed to eat and rest soon. When they came upon **Aur** Atoll, Lijebake found a lonely spot on **Bikien** Island. They spent the night, but before the sun rose from the ocean, Heavy Rain wanted to move on.

Lijebake said, "We can't just go."

"But, grandmother, they might find me . . . "

"We have to leave something for the people of

**Arno** AHR-noh

**Litakboki** lee-tahk-BOH-kee

**Aur** AH-oor

**Bikien** BEEK-ee-en

this place, to thank them for letting us stay," Lijebake told her. "We must treat them like family."

Lijebake left turtles. It was Lijebake who first brought turtles to the Marshall Islands.

**Erikub**
ER-ee-koob

On they swam to **Erikub**. Although many pandanus bobbed on the waves, Heavy Rain asked her grandmother, "Can we stop here?"

They spent only two days before Heavy Rain grew nervous again, afraid they hadn't gotten far enough away. Before leaving, however, she asked, "Should we leave turtles here, too?"

Lijebake was so happy she left lots of turtles. Turtles and turtles and turtles. Erikub is sometimes called Turtle Island because so many turtles are there still.

**Jemo** JEH-moh

When she sighted the small island **Jemo**, Heavy Rain cried out, "Look, grandmother, another island!" Together they visited the people of the island. Those Jemo people gave food to the two, inviting them to stay as long as they wanted. The next day turtles appeared for the first time on Jemo.

**Awon** AH-wohn

**Take** TAH-keh

So it went. Each island brought more happiness to Heavy Rain. And Lijebake brought turtles to every island. Ailuk and Utrik, **Awon** and **Take**. On and on they traveled until they were far from Kiribati, far away from Heavy Rain's family and far enough away from her fear.

That's when they arrived at Bikar.

**Jiadel** jee-AH-rehl

Nearly jumping off her grandmother's back, Heavy Rain looked for the people of the island. Before she found anyone, she found **Jiadel**, a place where only the chief can fish. When she set foot there, the sky burst open and rain and lightning poured out.

Across the island, the *iroij* told his people, "Rain. Go see if fish have come to Jiadel."

Lijebake stopped Heavy Rain from looking any further. "They will come. Now, if they give you anything to eat, throw it into the ocean and go straight to the chief. When you see him, clap your hands." Lijebake disappeared into the water.

"No fish," the people told the *iroij* when they returned, "but there is the most beautiful girl we've ever seen sitting over there."

"Bring her here!" the *iroij* cried. "Bring her here!" The people brought food from all over to welcome this beautiful girl to the island.

When the chief arrived at Jiadel, Heavy Rain did just as her grandmother said. At the sound of her claps, many, many turtles came to the island.

The chief gave Heavy Rain land there in Bikar. So she stayed. Her grandmother turned into a rock, which is still there.

*Bikar is known for having plenty of turtles. And, of course, rain.*

# RILE

**Rile** REE-leh

*mwio* [MWEE-oh]
a large fishing
net made out of
coconut leaf

**Kōtorlok Botoklok**
keuh-TOHR-
lohk BOH-tohk-
lohk

**Lōnen** LEUH-nen

**Kaben** KAH-ben

*mokan*
[MOH-kahn] a
food made from
cooked and
grated pandanus
wrapped in a
coconut leaf

*bubu* [BOO-boo]
magic

*There was a special kind of fishing net made out of coconut leaf called a "mwio." A whole group of people, even a whole island of people, fished together using the* mwio. *It was important that the people worked together to bring the fish to shore. They all fished for the* iroij, *who divided the fish among his people.*

On Ailuk Island in Ailuk Atoll, the people went out to a place called **Kōtorlok Botoklok** to fish with a *mwio*. They worked together, but one man kept taking the big fish out.

"Who's that over there taking out the fish?" **Lōnen**, the *iroij*, asked some people fishing near him.

"Your son," the people told him, "Rile."

Angered, the *iroij* called out, "You tell Rile his blood is in my hand."

When the people told Rile, he ran along the reef to **Kaben** Island. He ran to the home of his father's sisters.

"What's the problem?" Rile's two aunts asked.

"I took these from the *mwio*," Rile said, holding up the fish.

"Leave the atoll," the older aunt said. "Now. Your father will be here soon."

The other told him, "Gather some copra, quickly, while we prepare food for you."

The two women made *mokan*. Rile made *bubu*

with a leaf to see where he should go. The leaf told him to sail to Likiep Atoll, to the island of **Loto**. One of Rile's grandmothers lived there. His aunts gave him the food and Rile sailed off in a hurry.

Loto LOH-toh

When he arrived on Loto, Rile told his grandmother about the trouble.

"Stay at home," she told him, "Whatever you do, don't go running and hiding around the island. You have to fight."

As she said this, one of the Loto people saw a small group of canoes approaching.

"People!" Rile's grandmother said. "Rub oil on my grandson's body to get him ready to face those Ailuk men." She cast *bubu* to try and protect her grandson.

Rile's father landed. The men he brought from Ailuk were very tall, about eight feet each.

Rile, ignoring all his grandmother had done for him, ran off.

"Catch him!" shouted the *iroij*.

The men searched and searched the island, calling, "We're coming after you, Rile. Your father waits to fight."

At the end of the island the *iroij* put a large spear in the water, with the point facing toward the land. He planted it deep enough that no one could see it.

Rile tried to outrun and outhide those men. He ran to the end of the island, meaning to escape over the reef. But as he stepped into the water, he ran straight into the spear.

Rile stumbled out of the water, the spear stuck in his chest. He dragged himself back to his grandmother's house, where his father waited. When Rile got there, he pulled the spear from his body and died.

Rile's father, the Ailuk *iroij*, sailed back to his own island.

# JAKUNNE

**Jakunne**
jah-KOON-nay

**Kadjo** KAHR-joh

*On Kaben there's a special place for fishing called Kadjo. You can catch a lot of fish at **Kadjo**; you just have to be careful. When you're fishing with a pole, follow this rule: Never look behind you. No matter what, always look straight ahead as you cast the line.*

Whenever Christmastime came, the people from all over Ailuk Atoll visited the island of Ailuk for the festivities. Across the lagoon on Kaben Island, the people worked hard each year to get ready, cooking and drying food, fishing, and packing the canoes.

However, one year, a man named Jakunne didn't want to go. Jakunne just wanted to fish.

"Ssst! Jakunne!" his friends called to him as Jakunne worked his fishing pole. "We have to finish this sail."

"I'm tying my pole," was all Jakunne said.

"But it's almost time to go to Ailuk!"

When the people started loading the canoes, passing packages of food and gifts down a long line that stretched from shore to boat, Jakunne wasn't there.

"Jakunne!" someone called. "Come help gather the coconuts!"

Jakunne just said, "I'm cutting my bait."

When everyone waded out to the canoes, parents

carrying children, men carrying the old, Jakunne still hadn't appeared.

"Ssst!" the women called. "Jakunne! Jakunne!"

"I'm busy right now."

"But it's almost Christmas!"

"Never mind about that!"

The sails opened wide and the people of Kaben headed straight for Ailuk, singing of the upcoming festivities.

Except, of course, for Jakunne. He smiled, glad to be finally left alone. "I'm going fishing." He picked up his fishing pole and trudged off to Kadjo.

When he got to that special fishing place Jakunne didn't wait. He immediately cast his line. But the line immediately got stuck behind him. Hard as Jakunne pulled at it, he couldn't get his line free. As he struggled he heard a rustling in the bushes.

*Ekōbkōb, Ekōbkōb, Ekōbkōb kejen Jakunne.*
Bending, bending, bending the pole of Jakunne.

The line pulled Jakunne. Jakunne pulled the line. He stubbornly refused to let go. The struggle grew more intense, as did the rustling behind him.

*Ekōbkōb, Ekōbkōb, Ekōbkōb kejen Jakunne.*
Bending, bending, bending the pole of Jakunne.

Finally Jakunne turned to look where his line had snagged.

*Ekōbkōb, Ekōbkōb, Ekōbkōb kejen Jakunne.*
Bending, bending, bending the pole of Jakunne.

Two demon women jumped out of the bush and grabbed at him. "JAKUNNE!"

Jakunne dropped his pole and dived into the water. He swam hard, but the demons swam just a few feet behind him. "JAKUNNE!"

Jakunne dragged himself out of the water, the demons gaining on him. He scrambled across the island looking for a place, anyplace, to hide. The demon women kept screaming "JAKUNNE!"

At the first house he saw, Jakunne climbed into the **bo** and hid. Suddenly, it was very quiet. Jakunne hardly dared breathe. He waited till it got very dark, then peeked from out of the *bo*.

*bo* [bwo] rafters

"JAKUNNE!" The demon women screamed as they poked sticks into the ceiling, trying to kill him. Jakunne leapt from the roof and ran off, looking for help. But all the Kaben people had sailed off to the festivities.

Jakunne ran over the reef to the next island, and to the next. He ran from island to island to island, all along the atoll. The demon women wouldn't leave him alone; they just kept following and screaming, following and screaming.

Jakunne grew exhausted. The demon women got closer. Jakunne knew he couldn't outrun them forever.

Loujen
LOH-oo-jen

At an island called **Loujen** an old man and woman sat quietly outside their small home, weaving and working, when a frightened shout ripped through the air. "Deeeemon!"

The old woman screamed as Jakunne leapt out of the bushes and landed right at their feet.

The old man and woman leaned close to the body. Jakunne lay completely still, not even breathing. "Is he . . . ?" the old woman whispered.

Jakunne sucked in a huge breath of air, startling

12

them both. Through his breaths of air, he called out, " . . . mon. Deeemon!"

"Demon?" cried the old woman.

"Where?" the old man asked.

But Jakunne could only cough out, "Demons, demons," until he died.

The old couple buried him there, far from his home, far from the festivities. Jakunne was as alone in death as he had wished to be in life.

# AILUK

## KOJU ALFRED

**Koju** KOH-joo

Koju is the senior deacon for the Protestant church on Ailuk. While I was there, he led the church services, as the regular minister was in Majuro.

On the evenings that Koju shared his stories, we sat on mats in the main room of his house, leaning against the wall. He set up a light with a portable battery, as Ailuk (like most of the islands in the Marshalls) has no electricity. His wife, the *leroij* of the island, got us coffee and tea.

*leroij* [LEH-rohj] chiefess

On the first night, she showed us pictures from a trip she and Koju took to Missouri to visit their children. As they described the vacation, Koju mentioned stopping in Honolulu and seeing a play about

14

the Marshall Islands. It was a play I had written. Six years and several thousand miles later, I met my biggest fans.

Koju's family is from the atolls of Ailuk and **Aelōñlaplap**. He was born in Ailuk. His *joui* is **Jejjed**. He grew up with six brothers and six sisters.

When World War II came to the Marshalls, Koju was attending school in Ailuk. The Japanese moved him to Wotje to attend school. He lived with the Wotje *iroij*, because they discovered they shared the same *joui*. At one point during the war, the Americans bombed Wotje, not knowing that Marshallese were there. A whole group of Marshallese from Wotje escaped to the nearby island of Erikub late one night. They sailed by small outrigger canoes. They were on Erikub for three days before the Americans came and took them to Arno.

When the Japanese left, Koju remembers feeling excited and happy. He was on Majuro, where the people celebrated with a big rally. They rode around the whole island.

After the war, Koju went back to school in Ailuk. When he was nineteen or twenty he was selected to go to school in Majuro, but he was in love with his future wife at that time so stayed on Ailuk.

**Aelōñlaplap**
 eye-LEUHNG-
 lap-lap

**Jejjed** JEJ-jehr

**KOJU ALFRED**

# LUWAJWOJ

**Luwajwoj**
loo-WAHJ-wohj

**Bikon** BIH-kohn

There was an old man, Luwajwoj, who lived with his family on Bikon Island in Ailuk Atoll.

One morning Luwajwoj and the men of **Bikon** took a walk around the island. At oceanside they found drag marks. A sea turtle had come up on shore to lay eggs.

"Fifteen days," one man said. "We wait fifteen days and it'll be back."

Now Luwajwoj, he went back before fifteen days had passed. When he got there, he saw the turtle. He knew he wasn't strong enough to stop the turtle. He also knew if he left to get the others, the turtle would be gone. So Luwajwoj started digging a hole in the path of the turtle. He was still digging when the turtle slid right on past him and the hole. Luwajwoj ran ahead of the turtle and dug another hole, but the turtle waddled by that one, too, on its way to the ocean.

Luwajwoj picked up a rock. He hit the turtle. But it never seemed to feel a thing, just pushed on and on and on, closer to its ocean home.

Desperate, Luwajwoj took off his pants. He threw them over the eyes of the turtle and waited for it to stop.

The turtle didn't. It kept moving right at the old man. Luwajwoj tried to hold it back, but the turtle pushed the old man right out of the way! Luwajwoj dropped to the ground, panting, and watched as the turtle slid into the ocean, still carrying his pants.

Luwajwoj couldn't think of what to do. He didn't have pants. How was he to get home? Luwajwoj waded into the water. He walked along the shore hoping he might find someone to bring him pants. When he got close to his house, Luwajwoj called and called for someone to come.

No one came out. They all wondered why the old man kept yelling. The sun burned so hot that day, they wondered why the old man didn't just come back to his house.

Another old man went out to see. "What's going on, Luwajwoj?"

"I don't have any pants!"

"Where are they?"

"On the turtle. Can you get me another pair of pants?"

[Koju burst into laughter. He could hardly finish.] The old man was okay, he just didn't have any pants!

# RATAK CHAIN *Sunrise Islands*
# WOTJE

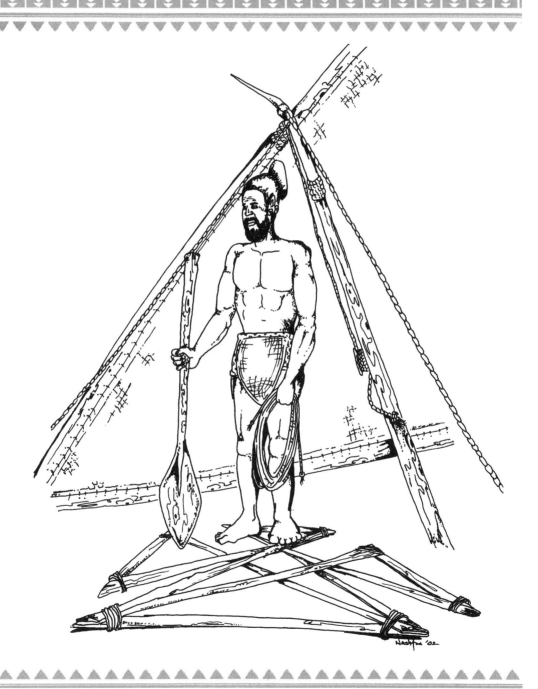

# WOTJE

## TONKE AISEA

**Tonke Aisea**
TOHN-keh eye-
SAY-ah

As is true of too many of the tellers in this collection, Tonke has since died. He was the very first
storyteller I visited, and at that time I had no idea
where my journey of story collecting would take me.
Unfortunately, I never got to interview him.

When I went to Wotje, I was there for only a day
and a half, so the very first night was story night. My
host spoke quite good English, but modestly asked if
he could tell the story in his native language. "Sure,
great, whatever you want!" was my answer. I was
too excited by the prospect of being there to care
about that right then. The sun had set, so a mosqui-
to coil was lit, and by the light of a dim lamp I set
my little portable tape player going and he started
in. What a great story. Classic. I didn't understand
the story yet, but just sitting there experiencing the
process of the telling was enough.

Tonke had learned the story from his grandmother. He said he vividly remembered listening to
her. He said he loved to tell stories to the children
of his island, though he didn't often get the chance.

**TONKE AISEA**

# TWO BOYS WHO TRICKED A TROPICAL DEMON

*Across the reef from my island is another called*
**Wōnbar**. *This story I tell happened a long time ago
on Wōnbar.*

**Wōnbar**
WUEHN-bahr

Two boys lived with their mother and father on
Wōnbar. They had no food. When they awoke each
morning, their food was gone. Every day the boys'
father had to find food for his family.

One morning the two boys ran up to their father
as he gathered his fishing net.

"Bring us **kōtkōt** birds," they asked him.

"The fighting bird!" said the younger boy. "We
want to see fights."

**kōtkōt**
[KEUHT-keuht]
a bird, the
ruddy turnstone

"And maybe we can help get food," added the
older.

"That's right!" the younger blurted out, all excited. "We'll capture eating birds. Lots and lots of eating birds. We'll have a feast every night and every
day and every . . . " He ran about imitating the fighting *kōtkōt* birds.

"All right, all right," their father said, and paddled off in his canoe.

After he had caught many fish, the boys' father
made a trap from a coconut shell and the rib of a
palm leaf. He hid behind a tree and in no time at all
he had trapped two of the fighting birds under the

shell. "That's good," he thought. "One for each of my boys."

As the sun slowly disappeared from the sky, the boys' father arrived back on Wōnbar.

"Boys!" he called. "Boys!" The boys appeared immediately.

"Did you get the birds? Did you get the *kōtkōt*?" the boys asked out of breath.

"Oh, yes," their father said, showing them the birds. "I caught two."

"Fighting birds!" the younger brother yelled out. "Let's go see some fights!"

"But before I give you these birds, you must promise never to take them to the north side of the island."

"Why?" asked the youngest.

His father paused a moment.

"Why? Why?" the boy repeated.

"Never mind," his mother told him. "Just listen to your father. Stay away from the north side of the island."

The boys agreed. They built a small cage for the *kōtkōt*, then went to sleep talking of the fights they might see the very next day.

The next morning, the boys woke early. They grabbed their new pets and headed to the east side of the island. Their father stuck his head out a window and called after them, "Remember, boys, don't go to the north side of the island!"

The boys nodded as they headed off, singing a song as they went. When they reached the east side, they discovered lots of birds.

"Eating birds!" shouted the younger brother. "We'll never be hungry again."

The boys let the fighting birds go. Just a glimpse

of the fighting *kōtkōt* in flight, however, sent every one of the eating birds screaming into the air as quick as wings can flap.

"That wasn't much of a fight," said the older boy.

"I thought we'd at least see some action," the younger said. "All we got to see was a bunch of chicken birds. Come on, let's follow them."

"Never mind. It's getting late," his older brother said. Disappointed, the two headed home.

The next morning the younger boy grabbed his brother. "Let's go out again. I bet we can find some tougher birds over there," he said, pointing.

"Sure, okay," said his older brother.

Father stuck his head out of the house. "Don't go to the north side, boys."

The older brother answered quickly, "Sure sure sure!"

The younger boy said nothing.

The two grabbed their birds and ran straight for the west side of Wōnbar.

There the boys stumbled onto more birds than they could eat in weeks.

"Let's take a rest first and then . . . " began the older boy, but his brother cut him off.

"I don't want to take a rest! I want to see some fights!" he shouted, as he ran toward the shore.

Startled by the younger boy's yelling, the birds leapt straight into the air and flapped off.

"No! Not again," the younger shouted. "Come on, this way. I'm not going home till we see some fights!" He grabbed his *kōtkōt* and ran after the cloud of birds.

"But brother . . . " the older started to say, "you're running to the north side."

But his younger brother had disappeared

between the coconut trees. The older boy sighed and ran after him.

By the time the boys got to the north side not a bird was in sight.

"I can't believe this!" shouted the younger brother. "Are we never going to see a fight?"

A voice from the bushes spoke. "I have fighting birds."

The brothers turned. There stood the demon of the north side of the island.

"Woo-hoo! Let's have a fight!" the younger boy shouted. "We've got the best fighting birds on the island!"

His brother, however, was more than a little scared. "Shhh, quiet!" he told his brother. "That's a demon. A demon!"

His little brother wasn't listening. "Our birds will shred your birds like coconut."

The demon chuckled, "Then we'll certainly have some fun!" Faster than lightning he grabbed the *kōtkōt* birds and ducked between the coconut trees.

The demon placed the fighting birds into a cage with his own birds. Immediately the birds attacked each other. They fought fast and hard, and in just a breath of time, the fight was over.

"Not one feather left," the demon whispered.

The younger boy grinned a huge grin. "Best on the island. I told you!" He slapped his brother's shoulder, but he wasn't smiling. He stared as the demon began turning colors.

"What's wrong?" the younger boy asked his brother. "We won."

"He's not laughing," he answered.

"You're not laughing," the younger brother said to the demon.

But it sounded more like "lafinkaaaa," as the demon grabbed the boys, lifting them as easily as two birds.

"It's your turn now," the demon told them.

"For what?" asked the older brother, rubbing his neck.

"To be eating birds," chuckled the demon as he dropped them into a deep, deep hole with nothing but a large clamshell sitting at the bottom.

And the demon said, "Show me your hands, boys."

The boys held out their hands, saying, "See our hands? They're very skinny. Unless they're fat you won't want to eat us."

So the demon brought them food, baskets and baskets of food to fatten them. The younger brother ate, glad for once to have so much. The older didn't. Instead he broke open the coconuts, emptied them, and pulled off the coconut hair. Rubbing it back and forth on his thighs, he rolled the hair into a long cord.

Every day the demon asked to see their hands, and every day the boys held them out. "See our hands? They're too skinny. Unless they're fat you won't want to eat us." And every day the older boy rolled and rolled the coconut hair.

Until one day the demon decided it was time to eat. "I'm making a cooking fire for you two boys," he called out to them.

The older brother grabbed his long rope of coconut hair and, looping the end, tossed it up into a coconut tree bending high above the boys' heads.

"The fire is leaping high, ready for you," the demon yelled.

The older boy climbed up into the tree. Then he lowered a basket for his brother.

"I'm coming, my eating birds!"

His younger brother quickly climbed into the basket, and the boy pulled him up.

"Here I am, little eating birds," the demon said as he peered into the hole. "Show me your hands."

What did the demon see? The two boys holding out their hands, of course.

"See our hands?" they said. "They're too skinny. Unless they're fat you won't want to eat us."

"You're fat enough today!" The demon laughed and grabbed at the two boys. His hands, however, grasped nothing but air, and he tumbled into the hole with a loud splash.

The older brother had filled the clamshell with coconut oil. The demon had been looking at their reflection.

High up in the tree the boys laughed. "We're slippery birds!"

The demon looked up.

"He's not laughing," said the older boy.

"You're not laughing," the younger shouted down to the demon.

"I'm not laughing," he said. "How did you get up there?"

"We climbed up using the roots sticking out of the dirt," the boys answered.

The demon tried climbing by grabbing the roots, but the roots pulled out of the dirt and he fell right back into the hole. The boys laughed harder.

"He's not laughing," said the older boy.

"You're not laughing," the younger shouted down to the demon.

"I'm not laughing. How did you get up there?" the demon asked through clenched teeth.

"We're just playing a little joke. We climbed up this rope." The younger brother let down the rope.

The demon climbed the rope. As he neared the boys, they dripped coconut oil down the rope. The demon slipped and slid down, landing in the hole once more. The boys laughed even harder.

"He's not laughing," said the older boy.

"You're not laughing," the younger shouted down to the demon.

"I'M NOT LAUGHING!" roared the demon. "Tell me how you got up into the tree!"

"Relax. We're just having fun. Really, we rode up in this basket."

The boys carefully lowered the basket. The demon climbed in. The boys pulled him up and up and up.

"Now I'm laughing," the demon chuckled, coming closer and closer to the boys. "And I am going to eat . . . " The demon grabbed at the boys just as they cut the rope. The basket crashed into the hole. The demon's head struck the clamshell and he died.

The brothers slid down the tree. They gathered up as much food as they could carry. The younger boy grabbed the fighting birds and the two of them ran back to their side of the island.

The boys' parents were surprised to see them. "We thought the demon had gotten you, had eaten you for his meal."

"We killed the demon!" the younger boy shouted out.

The older said, "There is so much food over there, we should live over there forever."

So they did and they had lots of food.

*I should know. They invited me to eat with them that day. If you ever stop by my island, I'll show you the hole where the boys stayed. It's still there on Wōnbar.*

# WODMEJ

## BOLDEN ELBON

**Wodmej**
WOHD-mej

**Bolden Elbon**
BOHL-den el-
BOHN

Since he was a young boy, Bolden Elbon has been dancing and singing. His grandmother taught him old songs and all the stories he now shares with his own family. The first song he remembers learning is about two girls who meet a dog while picking flowers. He sang for me the song the dog is singing when he meets the girls. The first story he remembers hearing is of the brothers named after birds.

Bolden's family is from all over the Marshall Islands, including Maloelap, Wotje, Ailuk, Utrik, Aur, **Jaluit**, Namdrik, **Ebon**, and **Kwajalein**. His grandfather on his mother's side came from Yap. He stopped in Jaluit during a trip and never went back home. He worked for the *iroij* there, who in turn gave him land.

**Jaluit** JA-loo-iht

**Ebon** eh-BOHN

**Kwajalein**
KWAHJ-ah-lehn

Bolden's grandparents and parents were diligent about teaching him the customs of the Marshallese. Bolden is adept not only at song, dance, and story, but also at building small canoes (he learned from his father's father) and making *aj*. In fact, Robert Reimers Enterprises (RRE) in Majuro, where he works as a security guard, made use of his *aj*-making skills when they expanded their hotel to include outdoor, local-style hotel rooms.

*aj* [ahj] the thatch
for roofs of
traditionally
built houses

He often teaches dance for special occasions to people from Wodmej Island in Wotje Atoll, where he was born and raised. He also creates his own songs and dances and teaches them to members of his church.

# LETAO

*What I know about Letao is from my father and grandfather. I heard them tell this story of Letao and* ***Jemeluit****.*

Jemeluit
JEH-meh-loot

Letao had a brother, Jemeluit. Letao and Jemeluit came from the Ratak chain, the island of Bikar. They grew up on many different islands, so once their mother told them to visit their Grandmother Turtle at Bikar. "Learn her power."

Letao challenged his brother, "The first one to Bikar gets the magic from Grandmother."

Letao leapt into his canoe and sailed off. Jemeluit wasn't far behind. They raced for Bikar.

Bikar Island was surrounded by huge waves and strong winds. Big rocks stuck out of the water. "We can't sail," Jemeluit called to his brother.

"Then swim!" Letao shouted over the wind.

Jemeluit dived from his canoe, kicking hard for the shore. The waves knocked him about. The wind blew him farther and farther from the island. Jemeluit got slammed into the rocks.

Letao helped his bruised brother climb into the canoe.

"We can't get the magic," Jemeluit said.

Letao felt sorry for Jemeluit. But not too sorry. "We'll be like Grandmother," he said.

"Grandmother's a turtle," Jemeluit said.

"You're smart, Jemeluit," Letao said. "So you can be a turtle."

"Why don't you be a turtle?" asked Jemeluit.

"Okay," answered Letao, "I'll be a turtle."

Jemeluit didn't trust his brother. "You're trying to trick me."

"I'm just going to be a whale," Letao told his brother.

"That's good," said Jemeluit. "I'll be the whale. Turtle's too small."

"Okay," Letao said. "I'll be the turtle." He smiled inside. He had tricked his brother again.

The two jumped out of their canoes and transformed themselves. When they popped up again, Letao-turtle and Jemeluit-whale set off for Bikar.

Letao-turtle swam slowly against the wind and the waves, watching Jemeluit-whale cut easily and quickly through the water. Jemeluit-whale leapt closer and closer to shore. Jemeluit-whale spouted in happiness.

But Jemeluit forgot about a whale's sensitive skin. The rocks scratched Jemeluit-whale and he fell back in pain. Letao-turtle had a hard shell. He rammed straight into the rocks but bounced off painlessly and continued straight to the shore.

Jemeluit-whale sank slowly under the waves, cursing his brother.

Letao-turtle wriggled onto the sand. He changed back to plain Letao. "Grandmother," he called, walking all about Bikar. He couldn't find her anywhere. Letao sat in the sand to think.

"You're on my back," the sand said.

Letao jumped up. He watched his Grandmother Turtle crawl out of her hole. "I beat my brother," he told her.

Grandmother Turtle looked up at Letao. "The magic is yours. Careful how you use it." She spit into Letao's mouth. "Now you can create anything you can imagine."

Grandmother Turtle gave Letao powerful magic. He could disappear, could change himself into a bird or fish. Letao became the first **dri-anijnij**.

*As the stories tell, Letao didn't always use that magic for good. Letao liked to play tricks and hurt people.*

*His brother, Jemeluit, became the first great chief of the Marshall Islands. But Letao never stopped picking on him.*

*Jidip inoñ jidim jedu.*
That's the end of the story.

**dri-anijnij**
 [ree-AH-nihj-nihj] magic-worker

**BOLDEN ELBON**

# FOUR BOYS CALLED BIRD

**Likāliklik** lee-
  KAY-lihk-lihk

**Kaekae** KAY-kay

**Kowak**
  KOH-wahk

*kiden* [KIH-ren]
  a flowering tree

**Kolej** koh-LEJ

There was an old couple living with their daughter Likāliklik on a small island. The great beauty of **Likāliklik** shined across the water.

There were four brothers living nearby, each on his own island. Each of the brothers' islands had only one kind of tree. **Kaekae**, the oldest, lived on an island full of pandanus trees. **Kowak**, the second, had only *kiden* flower trees on his island. **Kolej**, the third, had lots of coconut trees on his, and the youngest, Kōtkōt, his island grew only breadfruit.

The great beauty of Likāliklik struck each of the brothers to the heart. The youngest brother, however, was the first to try and claim the beautiful young woman for his own. So Kōtkōt picked a few baskets of his breadfruit and loaded them onto his canoe, and as he set off across the ocean, chanted:

> *Jekōkōke bar jet kā wa,*
> *wa bwilbwil tak iturin ettiet,*
> *wa bwilbwil ilo mejen.*
>
> *Likāliklik Likāliklik le . . . kweat in enin?*

*jekōkōke*
  jeh-keuh-KEUH-
  keh

> *Jekōkōke*! Here comes my canoe,
> My canoe passes over the blue water,
> My canoe sails onto the water black.
>
> Likāliklik Likāliklik . . . who is on the island?

The beautiful Likāliklik answered in chant:

    *Ña me jineo me jema.*
    Me and my mother and my father.

"Tell your parents I'm here to see you," Kōtkōt told her as he sailed to her shore.

But Likāliklik just ran to her house, telling him to go away.

The youngest brother felt ashamed. He sailed back to his own island.

Kolej saw his younger brother sailing in a canoe empty but for the breadfruit. So the third oldest of the brothers piled his own canoe high with coconuts and sailed off to the beautiful girl's island, chanting:

    *Jekōkōke bar jet kā wa,*
    *wa bwilbwil tak iturin ettiet,*
    *wa bwilbwil ilo mejen.*

    *Likāliklik Likāliklik le . . . kweat in enin?*

    *Jekōkōke*! Here comes my canoe,
    My canoe passes over the blue water,
    My canoe sails onto the water black.

    Likāliklik Likāliklik . . . who is on the island?

The beautiful girl answered in chant:

    *Ña me jineo me jema.*
    Me and my mother and my father.

"Tell your parents I'm here to see you."
Likāliklik ran to her house, telling Kolej to go away.

The third oldest brother sailed home, ashamed.

The second of the brothers, Kowak, saw his brother sailing home in defeat. He decorated his canoe with *kiden* flowers and chanted as he sailed off to make the beautiful Likāliklik his own:

> *Jekōkōke bar jet kā wa,*
> *wa bwilbwil tak iturin ettiet,*
> *wa bwilbwil ilo mejen.*

> *Likāliklik Likāliklik le . . . kweat in enin?*

> *Jekōkōke!* Here comes my canoe,
> My canoe passes over the blue water,
> My canoe sails onto the water black.

> Likāliklik Likāliklik . . . who is on the island?

The beautiful girl answered in chant,

> *Ña me jineo me jema.*
> Me and my mother and my father.

"Tell your parents I'm here to see you."
But Likāliklik told him to go away, too. Kowak dumped the flowers and left, ashamed.

The oldest of the brothers, Kaekae, had watched each of his younger brothers sail home, canoes empty. Kaekae, a beautiful man himself, filled his canoe with pandanus and sailed off, chanting like his brothers:

> *Jekōkōke bar jet kā wa,*
> *wa bwilbwil tak iturin ettiet,*

*wa bwilbwil ilo mejen.*

*Likāliklik Likāliklik le . . . kweat in enin?*

*Jekōkōke!* Here comes my canoe,
My canoe passes over the blue water,
My canoe sails onto the water black.

Likāliklik Likāliklik . . . who is on the island?

The beautiful girl answered in chant:

*Ña me jineo me jema.*
Me and my mother and my father.

"Tell your parents I'm here to see you."
"Okay," the girl said, "just wait over there."

You see, Kaekae was different from his brothers.
He had skin as beautifully colored as the bird that
now bears his name. So this time Likāliklik ran
straight to her parents, saying, "The beautiful one is
here. Kaekae. Come. Come and see him!"

Kaekae offered his pandanus to Likāliklik's parents. He asked them if she might come with him to
his island. Her father didn't really want her to go,
but the girl's mother thought it was a good idea. So
Likāliklik sailed with Kaekae to his pandanus-filled
island.

As they sailed, she pointed to an island and
asked, "Whose island is that?"

"Oh," said Kaekae, "that's the island of Kolej, the
one you didn't like."

At the next island, she asked again.

"The island of my brother Kōtkōt, who you sent
away."

"Whose island is that?"

"My brother Kowak, who you made feel ashamed."

When they finally arrived, Kaekae told Likāliklik, "Start a fire. I'm going off to fish."

However, Kaekae didn't fish. He caught two small lizards instead. He cut off the heads and tails and brought them back.

"For you, beautiful Likāliklik."

Likāliklik cooked and ate the fake fish before she noticed a piece of lizard skin there by the fire. Likāliklik got really mad. "Take me back to my island. Now!"

They sailed, but Kaekae stopped at the breadfruit island of his brother.

Likāliklik was not pleased. "I want to go home!"

**um** [oom] underground oven

Kaekae ignored her demands. He dug an **um** and tossed in some of his brother's breadfruit. Then he grabbed the girl and threw her into the *um* as well. Likāliklik screamed, but Kaekae paid little attention. After enough cooking time, Kaekae scooped out a basketful of the breadfruit-and-Likāliklik mix and carried it to the girl's island.

Kaekae offered the food to Likāliklik's parents.

The old man and woman thanked him for the food, asking, "Where's our daughter?"

"Oh, she's home, taking care of things."

Likāliklik's parents ate the food he had brought.

*And now you know what these four birds, Kaekae, Kowak, Kolej, and Kōtkōt, were up to before they became real birds.*

*Jidip inoñ jidim jedu.*
That's the end of the story.

# RATAK CHAIN *Sunrise Islands*
# MALOELAP

# AIROK

## HECEKEIA JIBBA
## JELJEL JERBAL

**Airok** EYE-ruk

**Hecekeia Jibba**
hes-eh-kAY-ee-ah   JIHB-bah

**Jeljel Jerbal**
JEL-jel jer-BAHL

**Tarawa** TAHR-ah-wah

Hecekeia Jibba and Jeljel Jerbal lived on the island of Airok in Maloelap Atoll. To get there, I had to fly to the island of **Tarawa**, Maloelap, disembarking near the shells of World War II Japanese Zero planes. Walking past the crumbling cement Japanese headquarters (now churches and homes), I went to the lagoon side of the island to await a tiny speedboat. A forty-five minute ride took me across the lagoon past the masts of sunken warships to Airok.

Airok is home to about 250 people. When I visited there, a restaurant had just recently opened. The owner was very proud of his small wooden hut that could seat maybe a dozen people. Each morning the older men of the island gathered there to drink coffee and eat pancakes. You could get soup there, too.

Hecekeia Jibba and Jeljel Jerbal were the only designated *alap* on the island. Hecekeia claimed the story of the pregnant girl is one of only two stories he remembered anymore. The other one he told featured the **rimenanuwe**.

*rimenanuwe*
[ree-MEN-ahn-way] the legendary "little people" of the Marshall Islands, similar to the leprechauns of Ireland or the *menehune* of Hawai'i

While Jeljel listened to Hecekeia tell the story of the little people, he made several corrections, claiming that Hecekeia didn't remember stories very well anymore. After I asked Jeljel about sharing his stories, we sat right down at the stoop of the house and he started. Jeljel's wife was in the background, relaxing on their cement floor (with a Bible as her pillow). At first he wanted to know what stories "the other old man" told. Jeljel then proceeded to tell his one story. Partway through the story he took out his razor and shaved as he finished the story. He finished both at about the same time. Jeljel told me that Airok had maybe ten stories altogether, but the demon one was all he knew.

As I boated away from Airok, my last image of Airok was Hecekeia fishing. He sat on a coconut with a long, nylon thread running from his fingers into the ocean. Both he and Jeljel have since died. No others have taken over the stories.

# BIRTH IS NO LONGER DEATH

On the island of Airok the women were few. Girls died giving birth. No one knew how to help them. When a baby was born, a woman died.

*mejenkwaad*
[MEH-jen-kwahr]
female demon

On the island the **mejenkwaad** were many. If a man went away before his pregnant wife gave birth, she'd become a *mejenkwaad* ready to devour her husband when he returned.

Only two women grew old on that island. They never gave birth. The old women collected the abandoned wives turned *mejenkwaad*. They treated them like daughters. Together they lived on the ocean side of Airok.

No one ever crossed to that side for fear of being devoured.

**Kañal**
KAHNG-ahl

At the middle of the island, the part called **Kañal**, there lived a different girl, a smart girl. She got pregnant and she didn't want to die. She ran away to the ocean side of the island. A big rock, the one that still stands, was there. The girl lay down and fell asleep under the rock.

When the girl woke up, the *mejenkwaad* were at the rock. They eyed the pregnant girl. The girl wasn't afraid, however. Maybe she was going to die anyway.

"I want to have a child. I want to hold the child," the girl said to the *mejenkwaad*.

They took the girl to the two old women.

40

"Oh, we must take care of that girl," said the two. "We must have our first child."

The two old women helped the pregnant girl give birth to a boy. They showed her how to give birth and live. She and her son went back to the middle of the island. The people there said, "We thought you died already."

When she showed her baby, the people spoke music and danced in their joy. The new mother taught the people how to birth. No more of the island's girls had to die.

# FISH, BIRD, AND CRAB

**Bub** buhb

**Barulep** bah-ROO-lep

**Ak** ahk

A demon man in Airok had three pets, **Bub** the fish, **Barulep** the coconut crab, and **Ak** the bird. He sang to his pets when it came time to feed them.

First, he sang to call their food:

*Jojo bāliktata jijjura na eo.*
*Kañe juon, kañe ruo, kañe jilu, kañe kañe ma ejjelok.*

*jojo* [JOH-joh]
 flying fish

***Jojo*** fish come jump up here.
Eat one, eat two, eat three, eat them all till there is no more.

*Jojo* flew onto the shore. Fish, fish, and fish, so many flying fish flew onto the shore, but the demon man took only three. He took them for his pets, always calling the fish first.

*Bubināne Bubin-meto kijem luj walok.*
Eh, fish, show yourself and eat your flying fish.

Barulep the crab came second.

*Barulep make kijem luj walok.*
Oh, big coconut crab, come show yourself, time for fish.

Finally the demon man called to his bird.

*Ake ie lōkōr im bōk kijem.*
Hey bird, fly over here and take your food.

It happened that way every day.

A lady lived in Airok, too, with her two sons, **Janinwe** and **Jamokro**. Every morning she told them to play at the south side of the island, not the north. Every morning they listened. But every morning they ran to the north side.

One morning they saw the demon man. They peeked from the bushes and saw him singing to the ocean. They saw all those *jojo* fish. They followed as he sang to Bub, Barulep, and Ak. They watched as the demon man left. Then Janinwe and Jamokro decided to try the chant.

> *Jojo bāliktata jijjura na eo.*
> *Kañe juon, kañe ruo, kañe jilu, kañe kañe ma ejjelok.*

> *Jojo* fish come jump up here.
> Eat one, eat two, eat three, eat them all till there is no more.

In flew the fish! So many fish came flying from the lagoon. Janinwe and Jamokro ate all the fish they could. They chanted again and the demon-man pets came, expecting to eat. The boys gathered them all up to surprise their mother.

"Where did you bring these things from?" she asked them, surprised.

"From the north side of the island," the boys said.

"But I told you boys . . . ," she started to say. The boys cut her off, saying, "Don't worry, the demon man doesn't know."

**Janinwe**
JAH-nihn-weh

**Jamokro**
JAH-moh-kroh

They had a flying fish feast.

When next the demon man called for fish, no
fish flew to shore. He sang again, but still not even
one fish. He wondered at that, but went off to call
his pets. Bub didn't show up either. Neither did
Barulep. And no matter how long he sang, Ak never
appeared. The demon man grew angry and went off
in search of his pets.

That same morning, Janinwe and Jamokro told
their mother, "We're going canoeing, to see if this
one is any good." You see, the demon man's
coconut crab was so big, they could use its shell for
a canoe. "If it works, we'll be going fishing."

"I'm afraid of the demon," their mother said.

"He doesn't know anything," the boys told her.
"But if he comes while you're fishing . . . "

So the boys put their mother high up in a tree.
They put the fingers of the crab up there with her,
so she'd have something to eat. They gave her a
coconut shell full of oil, too, just in case. The two
boys sailed off on the back of the crab.

The demon man searched everywhere. If he saw a
tree, he'd pull it out of the ground. If he saw a rock,
he'd toss it from where it lay. By the time he reached
the end of the island, the demon man was tired. He
took a rest under a ***kañal*** tree.

***kañal*** KAHNG-ahl

High above him, the boys' mother took a break
from mat making and ate a few fingers of the crab.
She laid the shells on her mat. When she started on
the mat again, the shells fell. The crab finger shells
landed on the demon man.

"Mmmm," said the demon man, looking closely
at the shells. "Mmmm, this is the finger of
Barulep."

Looking up, he saw the old woman. He tried to trick her. "Mother, mother," he called.

The woman looked down and saw him. "Mother, how did you get up there?" the demon man asked.

"I climbed," she told him.

"How did you climb?"

"Over here, I climbed here," she said, pointing up the middle of the tree.

The demon man climbed right there, but as he neared her, the woman spilled one of the coconuts of oil. The demon slipped, slipped, slipped all the way down to the ground. All the skin of his stomach and chest scraped off.

The demon man called again, "Mother, how can you do this to me? I can't climb because I hurt."

"Just climb with your back," the woman said.

So the demon man climbed up the tree with his back, but she dumped more oil down and the demon man fell again.

"Mother, you really don't care at all. How can I come see you when my back is all scratched up?"

"Okay, I'm sorry, my son, you can climb up on your side."

The demon climbed on his side. The woman spilled the oil. The demon man slipped down, scraping off the rest of his skin.

Angry and in pain, the demon man cried out, "The only thing left, Mother, is for me to eat this tree."

The demon man bit the tree. He bit and he bit and he bit. As he bit closer to her, the woman sang out to her sons.

*Janinwe ninwe Jamokro mokro*
*Jatin baru leb*
*Jinirnin jin ekojak tok kañel eo kañ jinmwi.*

Janinwe and Jamokro
Finger of the crab

The demon is eating the tree; soon it will fall
and your mother will be eaten.

The boys were fishing far out on the ocean. They
didn't hear her cry.

The demon chewed closer and the old woman
called again.

*Janinwe ninwe Jamokro mokro*
*Jatin baru leb*
*Jinirnin jin ekojak tok kañel eo kañ jinmwi.*

Janinwe and Jamokro
Finger of the crab
The demon is eating the tree; soon it will fall
and your mother will be eaten.

"Mmm," Jamokro said, "Mmm. I heard something over there."

"From where?" asked his brother.

"I don't know, I just heard about a tree falling
and eating our mother."

"That can't be. Keep fishing, it's a good day for fish."

Their mother called louder as the demon
chomped the tree into tiny bits.

*Janinwe ninwe Jamokro mokro*
*Jatin baru leb*
*Jinirnin jin ekojak tok kañel eo kañ jinmwi.*

Janinwe and Jamokro
Finger of the crab

The demon is eating the tree; soon it will fall and your mother will be eaten.

"I heard somebody calling our name, brother," Jamokro said.
"Nothing, it's just fish."

The boys' mother shouted as loud as she could over the demon man's last few bites.

*Janinwe ninwe Jamokro mokro*
*Jatin baru leb*
*Jinirnin jin ekojak tok kañel eo kañ jinmwi.*

Janinwe and Jamokro
Finger of the crab
The demon is eating the tree; soon it will fall and your mother will be eaten.

Jamokro said, "Mother is calling us. Do you hear it?"
"Okay," Janinwe said, "we'll see what's happening."

As the boys arrived at their island, the demon man took his last bite of the tree. Jamokro jumped onto the shore.
The boy and the demon man started to fight. The two fought from the ocean side to the lagoon side, tearing up the land. They fought from one end of the island to the other. They fought until the demon man died.

*Jeljel leaned out of his house and pointed. "The two boys and their mother lived right over there."*

# TARAWA

Kiat KEE-aht

## KIAT BENJAMIN

Jackning
JAK-neeng

I first met Kiat on a walk around Tarawa. He sat outside his small house with a whole lot of kids around him. My guide, **Jackning**, asked Kiat to go ahead and tell a story or two right then and there. It was quite a picture: he carefully told the story as all these kids circled around him like mosquitoes. It's a good thing I carried balloons with me that day. It made the kids happy to have something new to play with. It also made Kiat happy.

Kiat is devoted both to his church (he's a deacon) and his culture. He made it clear he wished younger people had more respect for Marshallese customs, as well as for God. He also developed a fierce dedication to bringing me stories. After the first session at his house he always took it upon himself to come to the local dispensary, where I was staying, to share stories. He was quite happy that I was collecting the stories, and even asked me to make a book of the stories to be able to share them with both Marshallese and Americans.

Kiat dropped by each day with a story or two. He even came by to listen to his longtime friend Jackning tell stories. Jackning and Kiat grew up together. You could tell, the way they both helped each other and joked around with each other.

Kiat is from Maloelap Atoll, where he has lived for most of his life, on Kaben, Airok and Tarawa Islands. He also has ties to Namdrik and Aur Atolls. His *joui* is **Makaulij**. When he was a boy, his grandparents took him from house to house to listen to the old people tell stories. He said he really enjoyed that time. "Many older people could tell stories then." He also said he enjoyed the times the community came together to celebrate in song and dance. Two particular events he mentioned were a day the Marshallese celebrated the older people of the islands, and the crowning of an *iroij*. He took part in the latter event on Kaben Island in Maloelap when he was thirteen or fourteen. He was one of a boys' group who wore woven *lauhala* hats and marched in celebration.

**Makaulij**
mah-KOW-lihj

At night Kiat tells stories to his children, or whoever wants to listen. However, he says, his children don't seem interested.

# THE Ụ

ụ [oo] fish trap

Eonikje eh-OH-
  nihk-jeh

*This story I'm about to say is about the custom of fishing with an ụ.*

This story took place on the island **Eonikje** in Maloelap Atoll. An old man and woman lived there. Every day the man put his ụ at the reef, oceanside. Every time he brought it back it was full of fish. He always took the fish to his wife to clean. Some fish they salted, some they preserved. They ate the fish with coconut, they ate it with breadfruit and banana. Every day the old man and woman had plenty to eat.

*"Your ụ is lucky if it's always full. But there's this custom for the wife of a fishing man. She's not supposed to clean the fish when her husband is out fishing. If she does that, well, I'll tell you."*

One day the woman was so very happy. Her husband had caught so many fish. As he went out to check the ụ a second time, the woman didn't wait. She cleaned the fish he had already caught.

A ten-foot shark came while the man was underwater. When the man came up, the first thing he saw, the very first, was his wife cleaning fish. Only then did he notice the shark.

The old man yelled, "Throw the fish at the shark. Throw the fish now!"

As we all know and understand, sharks are smart. This shark knew the old man was telling the woman a plan. When the woman threw the fish, the shark went for it, but when it heard the man walking on the coral, it swam at him and ate him.

*So that's something to remember. Don't forget the customs. If the woman had remembered, her husband would not have died. That's it.*

# MENENALUK

**Menenaluk** men-
en-AH-look

**Namu** NAH-moo

*lejale*
[LEH-jah-leye]
the *iroij*'s wife

*This story will be a little bit different from the other stories I told you. It's not from this island we are on right now; it's from **Namu**, the island of Deacon Ned and Johnson. This story tells about custom. When we were growing up, our grandparents told us about the* iroij. *They told us we must always talk quietly around the* iroij. *They also said a man must not talk to the **lejale** unless the iroij knows. Our grandparents told us we must always follow the customs. This story tells of a man who didn't.*

When Menenaluk was growing up, his grandmother and mother took good care of him. If they gave him a bath, they were careful not to break Marshallese custom. As we all know, if you give a bath with Marshallese medicine, you have to follow the right way. So they did. And this man, he grew, grew, and grew to be big, strong, and handsome. He grew up to be a giant. He could pull a canoe with eight or ten men on it. Whenever he walked, the island vibrated he was such a big man. A big hole would form in the sand.

One day, the *lejale* of Namu told the *iroij* she wanted to eat *jojo*, flying fish, from the reef at the south end of the island. As the sun set, the *iroij* gathered his men, including Menenaluk. "Whoever returns before me, pile your fish outside of my home and wait for me to return."

The men sailed off together as darkness fell. Menenaluk was gone only a short time before he caught a lot of fish. He returned while the rest still fished. The giant man piled the fish in front of the kitchen house and waited. The *lejale* saw him.

"Menenaluk," she called, "how did you catch all those fish so fast?"

"*Lejale, iakwe*," Menenaluk said. "These are for you."

They talked about the fishing and other things, too. After a while, Menenaluk decided he should leave.

"The *iroij* hasn't returned," the *lejale* said. She didn't want Menenaluk to go.

"Still, I'd better go." Menenaluk walked home, leaving his large tracks in the sand.

The *iroij* returned just before the sun rose. He went straight to sleep. The *lejale* gathered sand and rocks to cover the big man's footsteps. She didn't want the *iroij* to see the holes. When the *iroij* awoke, he wondered why the *lejale* was digging in the sand.

Every day the *lejale* asked for *jojo* fish. Every evening the *iroij* went fishing with his men. Every night Menenaluk always finished first. Every morning the *iroij* wondered why the *lejale* was digging in the sand. He also wondered why she always talked about Menenaluk.

"Menenaluk is your best man," she'd tell him. "He catches more fish then all the others."

"Menenaluk fishes so quickly," she'd say. "No fish seems to escape him."

The *iroij* wondered and wondered and wondered. Finally he decided to find out why all this strange behavior. After sending his men off fishing, the *iroij* hid and waited. Very soon Menenaluk returned with his large catch of fish. The *iroij* watched as the giant talked with his wife. He watched as Menenaluk went home, leaving large tracks in the sand. "Ah," he said, and went home to sleep.

The next evening the *iroij* blew his conch shell to gather his men to go fishing. As they left, he went to the lagoon side and caught some **no**. He placed them in the sand where Menenaluk always walked.

The *iroij* hid as Menenaluk returned. The giant man piled his fish. The *lejale* spent time with him. And

**no** [noh] a prickly sea creature

when Menenaluk left, he stepped on the *no*. The big man fell to the ground in pain, but he couldn't get the *no* out of his foot. The whole island quivered as the giant of a man died there in pain on the sand.

The *iroij* then chanted to remove the *no* from Menenaluk's foot.

> *Menenaluk ia,*
> *ekkā meto ie,*
> *no ie no ma,*
> *no ma jurjur ma jurjur no.*

> Menenaluk,
> Jump into the ocean,
> The waves are flowing,
> They keep coming, coming, and coming.

The *no* fell from Menenaluk's foot. "How come you're always hiding?" the *iroij* asked Menenaluk as the giant woke back into life. "I asked you to wait for me after fishing, but you're always gone when I return. What're you doing to me? Why're you always with my wife?"

Menenaluk said nothing. He had broken custom. The giant man leapt into the ocean and disappeared.

*If you go to Namu you'll see two reefs. The big reef is Menenaluk and the other is the* no.

# LŌBOKWA AND THE FOOLISH MAN

*This story I'm going to tell you this morning is about men who don't know how to take care of women. But you'll learn the right way. Listen to the story.*

At the time of this story, there were two small islands. One lay to the west; the other lay to the south. On the western island a woman named Lōbokwa lived with her husband and three children. On the other island lived only one man, a foolish man.

**Lōbokwa** leuh-bohk-WAH

As we all know and understand, women at that time took care of children, making mats and cooking for them. Men fished and gathered food. As we all know, at that time there were no cupboards; they put their food inside a ***bōjo***.

***bōjo*** [BEUH-joh] a basket

Now at that time the western island had no food. So Lōbokwa's husband fished all the time; he never stayed home. Every day, all day, he had to fish so he could feed his wife and children.

On the southern island the foolish man lived alone. His island had all the food he could eat and more, like pandanus, breadfruit, and taro. He never shared any with Lōbokwa's family. No, he just ate and watched as each day Lōbokwa's husband fished and fished and fished. But I will tell you one thing: this foolish man wished he had a wife.

Lōbokwa's husband soon became sick, really, really, really sick, headaches and body aches.

"Maybe an ocean demon got inside you," Lōbokwa told him. "You always spend so much time on the ocean."

He soon died, and Lōbokwa buried him close to the house. He left her with two small boys, a girl, and just one *bōjo* of fish.

The fish didn't last very long.

"Who will bring fish for us now?" Lōbokwa worried.

The foolish man began to wonder why he never saw that man from the other island anymore. So he sailed over by the western island. Sitting in his canoe, the man saw Lōbokwa and her children. He heard the children ask her for food. The foolish man turned his canoe around and paddled home.

*Now you will see why I call this man foolish.*

The man killed a pig and cooked it. He cooked up all kinds of delicious food. He put them in two **kilek** and sailed back to Lōbokwa's island. As the foolish man stepped onto the island, a bird flew over Lōbokwa's house, calling "*Kolej*! *Kolej*!"

**kilek** [KEE-lek]
a large basket

Lōbokwa sat inside with her hungry children. They cried when they heard the bird. Lōbokwa whispered, "Hush. Someone's here."

Outside, hidden behind a barren breadfruit tree, the foolish man started to sing,

> *Li-kirae ie Li-kirae*
> *rōbki menka kijen*
> *li-kirae, ie*
> *Li-kirae ie, Li-kirae*

*Lōbokwa kon droon to kejro*
*buki waj mōñā ke kijirjel.*

I sing to the woman with children, bringing
food to her.
I sing to the woman with children. Come outside, this food's for you.

"Here! We're here!" Lōbokwa answered, then
turned to her children, "Wow, see? Soon we'll have
food."
The foolish man just sang on, didn't move from
his spot.

*Li-kirae ie Li-kirae*
*rōbki menka kijen*
*li-kirae, ie*
*Li-kirae ie, Li-kirae*
*Lōbokwa kon droon to kejro*
*buki waj mōñā ke kijirjel.*

I sing to the woman with children, bringing
food to her.
I sing to the woman with children. Come outside, this food's for you.

"I'm coming, I'm coming." Lōbokwa saw the
man, his arms full of delicious food, as she stepped
out of her house. He just stood, not moving or saying anything. Lōbokwa reached out to take the *kilek*
of food, but the foolish man shouted at her.
"Eh! Go back in your house! How dare you take
this food from me!"
Lōbokwa, ashamed, ran back inside. The man
stared at her, then quickly sailed home.

Days passed. The poor children cried, hunger gnawing at them. The man didn't return. Then one morning the bird cried, "*Kolej*! *Kolej*!"

The children fell quiet. Lōbokwa thought, "Could it be him?"

> *Li-kirae ie Li-kirae*
> *rōbki menka kijen*
> *li-kirae, ie*
> *Li-kirae ie, Li-kirae*
> *Lōbokwa kon droon to kejro*
> *buki waj mōñā ke kijirjel.*

> I sing to the woman with children, bringing food to her.
> I sing to the woman with children. Come outside, this food's for you.

Lōbokwa and her children smelled the delicious gift.

> *Li-kirae ie Li-kirae*
> *rōbki menka kijen*
> *li-kirae, ie*
> *Li-kirae ie, Li-kirae*
> *Lōbokwa kon droon to kejro*
> *buki waj mōñā ke kijirjel.*

> I sing to the woman with children, bringing food to her.
> I sing to the woman with children. Come outside, this food's for you.

"Yes, I'm coming," Lōbokwa called. As she left the house, the man stopped singing. He just stared at her, holding all that food.

"Thank you," Lōbokwa said. She reached out gently this time, but still the foolish man shouted, "Eh! This is my food!"

The foolish man ran off quickly. Lōbokwa watched in surprise as the man dumped the food into the sea and hurriedly sailed away. Lōbokwa called to her children. They ran to save what little spoiled food they could. They devoured every last bit.

Of course, as we all know, this foolish man wanted a wife. But three days passed before the *kolej* came calling to Lōbokwa's house.

"Food, Momma, food," her children cried.

But Lōbokwa couldn't forget what happened. So she waited.

> *Li-kirae ie Li-kirae*
> *rōbki menka kijen*
> *li-kirae, ie*
> *Li-kirae ie, Li-kirae*
> *Lōbokwa kon droon to kejro*
> *buki waj mōñā ke kijirjel.*

> I sing to the woman with children, bringing food to her.
> I sing to the woman with children. Come outside, this food's for you.

Lōbokwa didn't answer him.

"Please, Momma," her children begged.

The man sang and sang and sang, three times he sang, but Lōbokwa refused to answer. After the fourth time, however, she couldn't ignore her children's pleas. Lōbokwa ran outside and tried to grab the food quickly, but the foolish man shouted louder than ever, "Eh! My food! My food!"

Off he ran, dumping the food into the ocean again.

"I'm not listening to that man anymore," Lōbokwa told her children as they gathered up the ruined food.

"Food, Momma."

"Hush up and eat."

As the sun set that very evening, as the small family finished the food, the boys heard something.

"Momma, the bird."

"So soon?" asked Lōbokwa.

"I don't hear it," the little girl said.

"*Kolej, kolej*!" the bird clearly cried, landing near the house.

"Not this time," Lōbokwa said. "We're not talking to him this time."

The boys ran outside.

"Come back here!" Lōbokwa called to them.

"It's only the bird, Momma," one said.

"It's nodding its head," observed the other.

"But no man," they said, disappointed.

"Come inside."

The sun disappeared. Through the darkness came a sound. The boys leaned out the window.

"Momma, someone's walking!" the boys cried.

"Ignore him," Lōbokwa answered.

"Food, Momma," cried her little girl.

A voice called out, "*Iakwe, iakwe*, are there people here?"

"The man!" the boys cried.

"Hush. Wait till he goes away."

"*Iakwe*," the voice called again.

The boys disobeyed. "*Iakwe*."

It was a man's voice. But not the foolish man.

*And now you will know and understand how to take care of a woman with small children.*

"Who's here?" the strange man asked.

"Just us," the boys shouted.

"Hush," Lōbokwa told them. "Come away from the window."

"Have you eaten?" the strange man asked.

"Not for months and months," said Lōbokwa's little girl.

One of the boys added quickly, "We only get garbage from the other man."

"Okay, wait," the stranger answered.

A strange noise, a ripping noise, came from outside. The children couldn't wait. They ran to the window to see. They saw this strange man pulling up some grass. As he did, a big hole, an impossibly big hole, appeared in the ground. The man jumped right in.

"He jumped in!" cried the little girl.

Before Lōbokwa could answer, the man crawled back out carrying a *kilek* of fish and a *kilek* of coconut.

"Oh," sighed Lōbokwa, "not another one."

But this man handed the food straight through the window. "Here. Eat. Enjoy yourselves."

We all know they did. But the man didn't stop. He pulled up breadfruit, chicken, and pig. Taro, papaya, pandanus fruit, and turtle. They ate and ate and ate until they were so full, so really full, they had to lie down to finish.

The man walked in, sat down, and watched them eat. When Lōbokwa finally looked up from the food, she saw he was very handsome.

*The man, you see, wasn't really a man. He was a*

**noniep**. *As we all understand, a* noniep *is a special spirit who comes to help people.*

Now this *noniep* told Lōbokwa and her children to take their time, relax. "I'll bring you some water, some **jekoro, jekajeje,** and **jakmi**, too."

He did, too, right out of the hole. They gulped it down as if they had never eaten in their whole lives. "Wow," thought Lōbokwa. "Wow. Where did this man come from?"

Every day after that there was plenty, plenty of food. Every day Lōbokwa and her children ate till they were really full. Every day the *noniep* stayed with them to make sure they were happy. And one day the *noniep* married Lōbokwa.

Now on that other island, the southern one, the foolish man felt so foolish. As we know, he wanted Lōbokwa for his wife, but every time the wrong idea came out of his mouth. He thought hard about it, then decided he should try one last time.

He sang as he paddled to the woman's island. He sang as he stepped out of his canoe. He sang as the *kolej* called out. The foolish man sang as he walked right up to the woman's house. He wondered why she didn't answer. He started to sing once more, then just shouted. "Come out here and get the food!"

Lōbokwa and her family stepped out of the house.

"Where did he come from?" the foolish man asked when he saw the *noniep*.

Lōbokwa told him, "You've treated us like we're not people, teasing us and then throwing away the food."

"Come," the *noniep* said. "Ignore him."

*noniep*
[NOH-nee-ep] a helpful spirit

*jekoro*
[JEH-koh-roh] fresh coconut milk

*jekajeje* [JEH-kah-jeh-jeh] coconut milk warmed under the sun

*jakmi*
[JAHK-meye] cooked coconut milk

**63**

"He's not supposed to be here!" the foolish man growled, growing very angry.

"He takes care of us," Lōbokwa said, as the *noniep* pulled her toward the patch of grass.

"Don't touch her!" the foolish man shouted, throwing the food at them. "She's mine! How dare you take her!"

The *noniep* pulled up the grass. Lōbokwa and her children disappeared.

The foolish man attacked their house, breaking it into small pieces.

The *noniep* stepped into the hole, closing it for good.

The foolish man ran off, shouting to no one, and sailed back to his own island.

*And as we all know and understand, that's the end of this story.*

**KIAT BENJAMIN**

# JEMENKUL

*You have to know how to respect the* iroij *and the* alap. *Our parents always taught us this. This story tells about one* iroij, *Jemenkul, of the Makaulej* joui, *and shows you how he was treated.*

**Jemenkul**
JEH-men-kool

*Iroij* Jemenkul and his two daughters lived on the small island of **Ejelben** in Maloelap Atoll, the storytellers say. Nearby lived two other men. **Tarkumar** lived on the small island called **Kumar** and another lived at a place called **Een**, meaning "small island." That man's name was La Een.

**Ejelben** eh-JEL-ben

**Tarkumar**
TAHR-koo-mahr

**Kumar** koo-MAHR

**Een** en

La Een fished every day. He caught all kinds of fish. He cooked, dried, and salted them. But he didn't give any to the *iroij.*

Tarkumar brought food to the *iroij* every week, as every good man should.

On Sundays *Iroij* Jemenkul would send one of his daughters to see if anyone was coming to visit from the other small islands. The girl always reported the same: "There's one man coming on the reef."

Jemenkul knew without looking, "It must be Tarkumar."

Each time, he told his other daughter to go and to make **mekwon**. It was a gift to a man who gave a gift. The girl mixed up two bowls, one for eating and one to drink.

**mekwon**
[MEH-kwohn]
boiled and grated
pandanus fruit

The *iroij* would keep asking his other daughter, "Where is he now?"

65

"Still coming, still coming."

Now when he arrived, Tarkumar carried all kinds of food with him.

"*Iakwe, iakwe, Iroij* Jemenkul," Tarkumar would say as he presented the food. "For you and your family.

"*Iakwe, iakwe,* my friend," the *iroij* would say in welcome. "Sit. Eat. Drink. You are a man who respects and should be respected."

Tarkumar always accepted the drinking *mekwon* from Jemenkul first and drank, drank, and drank. When he ate from the second bowl, he got so full the *iroij* would laugh and say, "Now relax, take a rest, and then you can go on home."

Sometimes *Iroij* Jemenkul would ask his daughter if she saw anyone coming from Een. Even though he knew this man La Een, the *iroij* would ask. The answer was always no.

This went on for years.

But one day, one surprising day, the girl came running back. "Papa, there is someone coming from Een."

"Oh, La Een," the *iroij* said, "the man who refuses to share."

The *iroij* told his daughters to make the two *mekwon*. When they finished, he carefully put the eating one in front with the drinking one right behind it.

When La Een arrived he called out, "*Iroij* Jemenkul, *iakwe*!" He had a lot of fish in his canoe, but brought none of it to the *iroij*. Not even the smallest fish.

"*Iakwe, iakwe,*" *Iroij* Jemenkul answered. "Is there any luck from you?"

"No, there's nothing," La Een said. "I have nothing. So I'm very hungry."

"Okay," the *iroij* told him, "if you say there's no food or drink where you're from, then come, here's some food."

La Een didn't even look; he just grabbed the eating *mekwon* and drank it. He drank, drank, and drank. He had to stop quickly, though, because he couldn't breathe. The eating *mekwon* was stuck in his throat. And right there he died.

*I tell you this story to make you think about respect.*

# TARAWA

**Josapeth Amram**
JOH-sah-bet
AHM-rahm

## JOSAPETH AMRAM

In 1999 I traveled to Tarawa, Maloelap, to collect stories. My schedule forced me first to fly to Kaben Island and hire a boat to cross the lagoon to Tarawa. It took us over three hours. And only after I got to Tarawa did I find out that the man who owned the boat was to share stories with me.

Josapeth is an entrepreneur. He has a couple of boats he uses to ferry people across the lagoon when they need to catch an airplane or visit a relative. He discovered his big boat, abandoned and full of fish. Because it's so big and comfortable, people asked him to give them rides, so he decided to make a business out of it. He says whenever Christmas or Easter programs take place on any of the islands, he gets really busy.

From the profits he's made, Josapeth bought a bicycle, a TV, and solar power. He plans to make his TV the local movie theater. He'll play videos, charging fifteen to twenty-five cents per person. He also sells sea cucumbers, which are popular with the Japanese.

Josapeth is an active teller, taking on the voices and physical characteristics of the different characters in his stories. I listened to stories in Josapeth's house, an old Peace Corps building from the early sixties that's shaped like a hexagon. A bunch of kids gathered as he told.

Josapeth's family comes from Namdrik, Mejit, Wotje, Arno, and Maloelap. His *joui* is **Debdeb**, which means "save your culture." Born on Tar Island in Maloelap, he grew up in Majuro, where he first went to school. He and his family moved to **Wollet**, Maloelap, but there was no school there then. When a school was built, he attended. He went to live with his grandparents on Majuro to finish high school, but returned to Maloelap to work for his family.

**Debdeb** REB-reb

**Wollet** WOHL-let

Both his grandfathers taught him stories. Every night, before going to sleep, he asked one or the other to tell a story. If they didn't come to him, he'd go to them. If he fell asleep while they were telling, they'd stop. The next night they'd ask him where they had ended the night before. Josapeth would tell what he remembered, and his grandfathers would finish the story. Josapeth is passing on the stories to his daughter and his son and his son's wife. They enjoy listening, he says. Every night they ask him to tell a story.

JOSAPETH AMRAM

# JENA, A BIG FART

**Jena** JEN-ah

*This story happened in the part of the Marshall Islands called* **Kaben Meto**, *the bottom of the ocean.*

**Kaben Meto** KAH-
ben MEH-toh

**Lojourur**
loh-johr-OOR

**Lojourur** stole Jena's wife. Jena chased after the wife stealer. Lojourur sailed from Kaben Meto to Aur, Ailuk, Utrik, and Wotje with Jena's wife. Jena followed closely in Lojourur's wake, but lost him. Jena brought his canoe to rest at Kaben Island in Maloelap.

**Okono**
oh-koh-NOH

Jena and his men, **Okono** and **Okona**, walked the reef to **Jang** Island. He asked the people there, "Do you know this guy Lojourur?"

**Okona**
oh-koh-NAH

**Jang** jahng

"Oh yes," those people said, "we definitely know this man."

"Where is he now?"

**Jabōnbok** JAH-
beuhn-bohk

"Wollet Island, the village of **Jabōnbok**."

Jena, Okono, and Okona crossed the channel to Wollet.

Jena didn't want to be recognized. At a big sandy place called **Bokenjine**, Jena removed his skin. But he left the birthmark on his chest.

**Bokenjine**
BOHK-en-jih-
neh

*They call it a* **jao** *on the Ralik side of the Marshall Islands, an* **ilemej** *on the Ratak side.*

**jao** [JAH-oh]
birthmark

**ilemej** [ee-LEH-
mej] birthmark

He told Okono and Okona to wait for him at a coconut tree on the reef. "Listen carefully for me."

Jena-without-his-skin walked to Jabōnbok. He saw Lojourur working in his canoe house. Jena's wife sat nearby.

"*Iakwe, **rittoro**,* husband and wife," Jena called, disguising his voice.

*rittoro* [rih-TOH-roh] people long ago

"*Iakwe, iakwe,* stranger," the two said. Lojourur added, "How did you come to my house, stranger?"

Jena grumbled, deep in this throat, "Okono. Okonaaa."

Jena's stolen wife peeked out of the canoe house. "Hey," she said, surprised, "it looks like my husband."

Lojourur laughed, "I cut Jena into pieces."

"*Iakwe, rittoro,*" Jena called again, a little more forcefully.

"*Iakwe, iakwe,*" the two answered, and once again Lojourur asked, "How did you come here, stranger, with whom?"

"Ookoonoo. Ookoonaaa," Jena growled, stepping close to where his wife peeked out.

"That's him. I know its him," Jena's wife cried. "I saw his *jao.*"

"You're crazy. I killed Jena. He's dead," he told her and called out, "How did you come here?!"

"Ooookooooonooooo! Ooookooooonaaaaaa!" Jena growled, grabbing the canoe in his anger. He swung the canoe at Lojourur.

Lojourur said, "Jena."

Jena's wife ran into the house and grabbed a drum. She started to play and sing. When a woman plays the ***adje***, it's time for a fight to begin.

*adje* [AHD-jay] drum

*If you want to know the dance with the drum, ask the women in Wollet to teach you. There is a woman called **Lijoko**. She really knows the dance.*

**Lijoko** lee-JOH-koh

71

Lojourur ran off as fast as he could. "Ooookooooonooooo! Oooookoooooonaaaaaa!" Jena growled again, smashing the canoe. Lojourur was so very scared, he messed his pants.

*The coral reef you see at the lagoon side of Wollet, that's Lojourur's mess. It used to be all sand, but not anymore.*

**Kabōredkoj** kah-beuhr-ER-kwoj

The frightened Lojourur ran all the way to **Kabōredkoj** at the end of the island. Right there, at the very end, he farted and flew into the air. Burrruuuuuup! Lojourur kept farting and flying until he disappeared into the sky.

*And now, today, the thunder you hear in Wollet, that's Lojourur farting. Burrruuuuuup!*

Jena stayed with his wife at Maloelap. He stayed there with his friends, Okono and Okona.

***karuk*** [KAH-ruhk] a small crab

**Aeninjena** EYE-nihn-jeh-nah

*Jena is a **karuk**. You know this because he can remove his skin like the crab. He now lives in the ocean at a place called **Aeninjena**. Navigators who pass this place know that Maloelap is close. They know, too, if you pass over Aeninjena the boat will break. They avoid it.*

JOSAPETH AMRAM

# KŌBELOKIE—BANISHED FROM HOME

*[As Josapeth started this story, a small child crawled into his lap with a great big yawn.]*

*This story is from Utrik, about the* iroij *and the* lejale.

The *lejale* was pregnant. Nine months had already passed but she hadn't given birth. The *iroij* felt very afraid of his wife. Her stomach grew so big, and her neck, feet, and arms kept getting smaller. He grew so scared he called a meeting of his *alap*, the old men of power.

"What should I do about the *lejale*?" he asked them. "Maybe she's turning into a *mejenkwaad*. Maybe she might eat us!"

The *alap* thought, thought, and thought, for a long time they thought. The *iroij* sat, shivering in fear. Then one *alap* suggested they should just bury her, and a second thought it smart to kill her now, but the *iroij* wouldn't hear of any of it.

"If she's a *mejenkwaad*, she might come back."

Finally one of the older *alap* suggested *kōbelokie*, an idea he'd heard from his visits to other islands. "Put her on something that floats. Set her off on the ocean."

The *iroij* immediately called his people to bring lots and lots of **waini**. They tied them together to make a **tōra**.

The *iroij* called for men to bring the *lejale*. But he

**kōbelokie** keuh-beh-LOH-kee

**waini** [weye-NEE] fallen coconuts

**tōra** [TEUH-rah] a raft of coconuts

didn't go. He watched from a safe distance as the men set her on the *tōra* and pushed her off onto the ocean.

For weeks and weeks and weeks the *lejale* floated. She landed on a barren island, not a tree to be seen. Although tired and hungry, she dragged the *tōra* onto shore. Half the coconuts she planted, and half she kept to eat.

Every day breadfruit or pandanus washed up on the *lejale*'s island. She planted anything she could. After days and days and days it started to look like a real island. Only then did she give birth. The *lejale* now had a family of six girls and six boys.

The *lejale*'s children grew and grew and grew with the island. One day, the oldest son decided he wanted to see more than just this island. He gathered his brothers to make a **tibnol**. The *lejale* told her daughters to make an **ujelā** for their brothers.

*tibnol* [TIHB-ngol]
a large canoe

*ujelā* [OO-jeh-leye] a sail

When the brothers had finished, the oldest decided they should practice sailing.

"Okay, my sons," the *lejale* said. "But practice only on the south side of the island. Do not practice to the west."

The boys sailed out, passing all the islands around the south side of their island. When night fell, they sailed home and went to sleep.

The next day they all wanted to go out again.

"Just remember, boys, practice on the south side of the island only," the *lejale* reminded them.

For four days they practiced. For four days their mother reminded them. And for four days they sailed around the south side only.

Finally the fourth oldest son said, "I'm getting tired of the south side. Let's go west."

A younger brother said, "Mother will be very mad."

"Don't worry," said the oldest, for he, too, felt bored. "We'll go to the south first and when mother can't see us anymore, we'll turn west." They went south, and when their mother could no longer see them, they turned their canoe west.

The boys sailed and sailed and sailed, sailed until the sun was setting. They sailed right close to Utrik. There the brothers saw a group of canoes getting ready to go *jojo* fishing. They didn't know, but those canoes belonged to their father.

The brothers decided to get a closer look. The oldest told them, "Nobody say a thing. I'll do the talking."

One of the Utrik men pointed out the strange canoe.

The *iroij* told his men, "No one talk. I'll be the one to do the talking."

When the brothers sailed close, the *iroij* called, "*Wa ta ne oh*? Whose canoe is this?"

The oldest answered, "*Añ jen rak jen*. From the north and the south."

The *iroij*, angered, called,

> *Etke kwoj illilok lik im man?*
> *Ewi jeman rokin ane?*
> *Ewi jeman rikin meto?*
>
> You're making fun of me?
> Where's your northern father from?
> Where's your southern father from?

The oldest only chanted:

> *Enne maan enne,*
> *Lik enne ilo baktok ne,*
> *Ilo dibin kiju ne,*

*Libbede luw wa,*
*Jarom! Jatel! Jako!*

He's at the front,
He's at the back,
He's at the place in the middle,
He's in the sail,
Boom! Bang! Gone!

The brothers sped off faster than the wind. The *iroij* nearly burst. "They talked back to me! We'll go fishing again and again and again to find out who those boys really are."

The boys arrived home and went right to sleep, telling their mother nothing. When they sailed off to practice the next day, their mother reminded them once again. But of course they headed west.

When they reached their father's island, the oldest said, "Nobody talk."

When one of the Utrik men saw the brothers' canoe, the *iroij* said, "I'll be the one to talk."

The canoes met. The *iroij* called, "*Wa ta ne oh*? Whose canoe is this?"

The oldest answered, "*Añ jen rak jen*. From the north and the south."

The *iroij*, angered, called:

*Etke kwoj illilok lik im man?*
*Ewi jeman rokin ane?*
*Ewi jeman rikin meto?*

You're making fun of me?
Where's your northern father from?
Where's your southern father from?

The oldest only chanted:

*Enne maan enne,*
*Lik enne ilo baktok ne,*
*Ilo dibin kiju ne,*
*Libbede luw wa,*
*Jarom! Jatel! Jako!*

He's at the front,
He's at the back,
He's at the place in the middle,
He's in the sail,
Boom! Bang! Gone!

Once again the boys sped off.

"Where is that canoe from? What island?" the *iroij* shouted. "I have to know!" He called for a man to blow the **jilel**.

"Bring the best **dri-bubu**!" he demanded of his people. "Bring the best navigators, the best canoe trackers, because I have to know who is out there!"

When the boys returned this time, their mother asked, "Why are you boys gone so long each day?"

The boys just said, "We catch a lot of fish and kinds of things."

They went to sleep without saying another word. The next day they lied to their mother again and sailed west.

The brothers met their father once again. They teased him once again. And once again they sped off with a boom, bang, gone!

But the *iroij* stood ready. He had gathered his best men. He shouted, "Take me where that canoe goes. Now!"

The brothers' canoe sailed very far very fast, but the *iroij*'s best men followed the canoe's wake.

The boys arrived home shouting, "Canoes are coming!"

**jilel** [JIH-lel]
conch shell

**dri-bubu**
[ree-BOO-boo]
sorcerer

"What are we going to do, Mother?" asked the youngest boy.

"Why didn't you boys listen to me?" the *lejale* answered. "Stay inside the house. Nobody talk, nobody say anything, nobody move."

The *lejale* stomped once, quite hard, and the island instantly became a mountain.

The *iroij* and his best men arrived. They wondered at this tall island they had never seen.

"Stay with the canoes," the *iroij* said. The mountain was tall, but a pandanus branch hung low. The *iroij* pulled himself slowly to the very top. There he saw the woman who had once been his wife fanning herself.

"*Iakwe* to all the people here!" he said, not at all recognizing her.

The *lejale* said nothing. The *iroij* repeated his greeting. She just sat. A third time he greeted her, but received no answer.

The *lejale* started to fan quicker. A cloud floated by. A wind whipped up. It rained and the wind blew. The *iroij* just stood and repeated his words. He shivered from the rain and cold, but still he waited for an answer. The *lejale* only stared, fanning. The *iroij* passed out.

The *lejale* called to her sons and daughters. "This is your father."

The boys were completely surprised. "Oh. Well now we feel sorry for him."

Their mother told them, "Bring him here, close to me." She fanned him, chanting:

> *Ine drele drele,*
> *Ine bokeboke,*
> *Konañin kule eo, kule eo ke?*

I fan him,
I hit him,
I ask, "Do you recognize me?"

The *iroij* blinked. "I do."
She asked, "Who am I?"
"My sister?" he said.
"Eh, I'm not your sister. Is your sister the one you put off to sea?"
The *iroij* passed out.
The *lejale* fanned him and chanted once again:

*Ine drele drele,*
*Ine bokeboke,*
*Konañin kule eo, kule eo ke?*

I fan him,
I hit him,
I ask, "Do you recognize me?"

The *iroij* pulled himself up, answering, "I know you."
"Who am I?"
"My mother?"
"Eh, I'm not your mother. Did you put your mother off in a *tōra*?"
The *iroij* passed out.
Once again she fanned and chanted:

*Ine drele drele,*
*Ine bokeboke,*
*Konañin kule eo, kule eo ke?*

I fan him,
I hit him,
I ask, "Do you recognize me?"

The *iroij* stood up, saying, "Yes, I do know you."

"Who am I then?"

"The wife for whom I sorrow."

"I thought you would never know."

The *iroij* sent for his men. They stayed at that island, now known as Mejit, and had a big celebration.

*They invited me to come and eat with them, but I said no, because Dan and Sylvia are getting very tired of waiting for me to tell a story! [He boomed with laughter, almost waking the child sleeping at his knee.]*

## McKay Langmouir

Langmouir
LAHNG-moh-
eer

McKay and his wife aren't able to get around much anymore. Age and lack of medical attention have taken their toll. McKay was possibly the oldest storyteller I talked with. He, like many others, said it was hard to remember. And he didn't want to tell any stories he only remembered a little of.

I listened to a few stories one afternoon in his home, a one-room cement-block house about the size of a large American living room. The room was clean and empty. Everything was cleared from the middle. All their clothes were inside a few suitcases lined up neatly against the wall. As McKay told, his wife sat in the background, occasionally eating a breadfruit someone had brought her, sometimes picking up a little of the garbage she saw near her. His telling was measured, with fairly long pauses and moments of thoughts. As he told, however, he warmed up and became more animated.

McKay traces his family to Namdrik and Maloelap. His *joui* is **Ri-kwoj**. When he was growing up, there were only two schools in the outer islands, one in Wotje and the other in Jaluit. He attended the one in Wotje.

When the Japanese came, McKay worked for them, like most Marshallese. He helped build several of the big cement houses the Japanese used for living and military headquarters. He said it was hard during that time, because he was treated like a slave. "If the men didn't do the work," McKay said, "they got punished."

When the war broke out, McKay had to look for American airplanes so the Japanese could shoot them down. He said it frightened him. He ran away like many other Marshallese and, like the others, ended up on **Tutu**, Arno. "America!" McKay joked.

**Ri-kwoj**
ree-KWOHJ

**Tutu** TOO-too

# TOLEWE AND THE BIG BIRD

*This story I will tell you is about two people, Tolewe and his wife, **Lijeia**. They lived with his mother, **Limarien**, on a small island in Arno Atoll called **Lōññar**.*

One morning at low tide, Tolewe noticed the coral reef called **Limjalulu** sticking out of the water. "Time for clam fishing," he said to himself, so he took an empty *kilek*, a basket, and slid his canoe into the water.

At Limjalulu, when he dived, a woman swam out from underneath the reef to greet him. Tolewe asked her permission to fish for clams. She agreed. He filled his canoe with clams, clams, clams, and clams until his canoe barely stayed afloat. When he arrived home, Tolewe had to call his wife to help pull the heavy canoe back onto shore.

Each day Tolewe collected clams and clams and clams. He was so lucky that, one day, his wife asked if she could come along. Tolewe agreed. So Lijeia made some perfumed coconut oil to take with her. She mixed into the oil some *kiar*.

Kiar *smells so very good, better than what the **ribelle** brought over here.*

"If you oil your hair," Tolewe told his wife as they reached Limjalulu, "be careful not to spill any

**Tolewe**
TOH-le-weh

**Lijeia** lee-JEYE-ee-ah

**Limarien** lee-mahr-ee-EN

**Lōññar** LEUHNG-ngahr

**Limjalulu** lihm-JAH-loo-loo

*kiar* [keeahr] perfume made from shark

*ribelle* [rih-BEL-leh] foreigners

in the ocean." With that he dived into the water.

Lijeia untied her hair, letting it flow over the edge of the canoe. She applied her sweet-smelling perfume carefully, remembering her husband's words. Still, some dripped into the water. As she slowly combed oil through her hair, the spilled perfume floated all the way to Majuro and Jaluit Islands.

The fishermen of those islands smelled the perfume. They became very excited. Leaping into their canoes, they paddled off after that sweet, sweet smell, chanting:

> *Wa eo ebwil im kōrtak ailik eo boñ eo.*
> *Waan āñ ah waan rak waan manini kileel*
> *buñ bātli aunōnōn,*
> *O eo in le kōrōne aunōnōn.*

This canoe follows the sweet perfume to the island.
Canoe from the north, canoe from the south.
The men of the canoe paddle,
O, they paddle.

The Majuro men paddled so hard their canoe broke. They had to stop at a small island called Manini. The Jaluit men chanted on, paddling hard:

> *Wa eo ebwil im kōrtak ailik eo boñ eo.*
> *Waan āñ ah waan rak waan manini kileel*
> *buñ bātli aunōnōn,*
> *O eo in le kōrōne aunōnōn.*

This canoe follows the sweet perfume to the island.

Canoe from the north, canoe from the south.
The men of the canoe paddle,
O, they paddle.

The Jaluit men reached the end of the oil trail. They found Lijeia still combing her hair. They grabbed her and sailed back toward home.

Before the Jaluit men even arrived, however, their *iroij* had heard about the sweet-smelling visitor from Limjalulu. When the men finally arrived, the *iroij* immediately claimed her for his own. He took Lijeia to his house, calling all the Jaluit women to sit with her.

Back at Limjalulu, Tolewe surfaced. He felt Lijeia's oil on his skin. He knew someone had taken her. He knew he had to find her.

Tolewe made a big, big bird from the wood of the **kōnat** tree. He chanted, sending it sailing into the sky.

*kōnat* KEUH-naht

> Float into the sky,
> Flap your wings.
> Go on over,
> Come on back.

The wooden bird flew only a short bit. *Kōnat* wood wasn't such good wood. Tolewe built a second one, this time from the **koñal** tree. He covered it in feathers and sent it off on a practice flight.

*koñal* KOHNG-ahl

> Float into the sky,
> Flap your wings.
> Go on over,
> Come on back.

The *koñal* bird flew a beautiful flight. "This is the bird," Tolewe said as he climbed in through a little doorway he had built for himself. "This is the bird that'll find my wife."

Tolewe and the wooden bird sailed off. He flew straight for Majuro, but Tolewe didn't see Lijeia anywhere. He flew, flew, flew, and flew from Majuro far to the north, all the way to Bikar. Still not seeing his wife, Tolewe turned south. As he sailed on across the sky, he chanted:

> *Kōkelōk jen armij in āne eo,*
> *Ij kakien bion ij io ia on*

> Sailing over the people of the islands,
> I wonder if I can ever find my wife.

Tolewe searched everywhere. People of each island came out of their houses to stare at the giant bird. Wotje and Bikini, **Rongelap** and Ujae, **Lae**, Namu, Aelōñlaplap, plenty of people on each, but Tolewe didn't see his wife on any of them. Finally Tolewe flew over Jaluit. There he saw Lijeia sitting with the *iroij*'s women.

**Rongelap**
ROHNG-eh-lahp

**Lae** leye

Tolewe landed his wooden bird on the *iroij*'s house. Everyone there shouted, pointing. The *iroij* rushed out of his house. When he saw the big bird he said, "Don't touch that bird. That's my bird. Leave it right there."

Night came. Everyone fell asleep. The little door on the bird opened. Tolewe slipped out and quietly called to his wife. "Ssst."

Lejeia woke up.

"Ssst."

She moved close to where her husband hid, careful not to wake the other women.

"I'm in the bird," Tolewe whispered. "When I call out, the bird is hungry. Get fish. Lots of fish."

Tolewe crawled back inside the bird. Lejeia went back to sleep.

The giant bird cried loud, "Laaaaa!"

The people all jumped from their sleeping mats.

The *iroij* came running out of his house. "What is that?"

Lijeia spoke up. "The bird is hungry. You need to bring fish, plenty of fish."

The *iroij* blew his *jilel*, his conch shell, calling together his men.

"My bird is hungry," the *iroij* told them. "Bring fish for my bird."

Just as they went, the bird cried again, "LAAAAAA!"

"What?" the *iroij* asked Lijeia. "What now?"

"He's really hungry," she told him. "He wants all the men on the island to go."

The *iroij* blew the *jilel* again. The rest of the men came. He told them to sail straight to the *iroij*'s own fishing spot.

As they left, the bird cried again, "LAAAAAAAAAAAAAAAAAAAA!!!"

"What?!" the *iroij* asked. "What? What?"

"All the men," Lejeia said. "You, too."

"Anything!" the *iroij* said. "Bring my canoe!"

The men brought it. The bird continued to cry.

"Whatever you catch, give it to that bird," the *iroij* said as he paddled off with his men. "Don't hold anything back."

When the *iroij* was out of sight, the little door opened. Lijeia crawled into the bird. Together, she and her husband flew off. As they sailed over each canoe, Tolewe cried, "Laaaaaa!"

The men threw fish, all their fish, up to it.

The giant wooden bird sailed past the *iroij*'s canoe.

"LAAAAAAAAAAAA!!!"

"Throw all the fish," the *iroij* cried. "All the fish!"

The bird snatched up the fish and sailed away.

Tolewe and Lijeia crawled out and sat on top of the bird.

"My bird!" the *iroij* shouted. "My wife! My fish!"

The happy couple flew back home to Lōññar.

*When navigators are sailing from Arno to Jaluit and see oil flowing, they know Jaluit is close.*

# WOLLET

## JACKNING JAJŌÑ

On my boat ride from Kaben Island to Tarawa Island in Maloelap Atoll, we stopped at the small island of Wollet to pick up Jackning Jajōñ. I didn't know at the time, but Jackning was coming to stay on Tarawa just for me. His daughter lives on Tarawa, and he stayed with her, but he agreed to become both my guide and one of my storytellers for the week I visited. He showed me around the island, which is filled with Japanese military relics, from rotting Zero planes to a hole in the ground where people were beheaded.

Jackning, with his big, bright smile and rich voice, told long stories. He liked to practice before being recorded, so we'd listen to each story twice.

His patience with details made for some great story-telling sessions. Like his good friend Kiat, he quietly signaled to me at the end of stories to turn off the tape recorder, being careful not to ruin the recording.

Jackning was born and grew up on the island of Airok in Maloelap, with nine brothers and sisters. One of his best friends was Kiat, who is also of the Makaulij *joui*. "Sometimes we fought, sometimes we set dried panadus leaves on fire and threw them at each other, but now we take care of each other." His grandfather told him stories every night, he said, "because they are one of the important things about our culture. The stories tell us how to respect sisters and mothers, how to treat the *iroij*, which *joui* belongs to what island, and how to live a good life."

When Jackning was still very young, the war came to Maloelap. His parents described the bombs as they dropped because he was too small to see them. He remembers having to escape the island to go to Aur, because "the Japanese had decided to kill us all so they could have the food and water on the island." During the family's escape a big wave filled their boat with water. The navy picked up all the people who had escaped and took some to Majuro and some to Arno. They lived in tents built by Americans. Jackning thought it was America because of all the lights and movies and boats.

# JAB BO KAKE—NOT LISTENING TO SOMEONE

*jab bo kake* [jahb boh KAH-kay] not listening to someone

**Ieb** yeb

On the island **Ieb**, a woman gave birth to twelve boys. Each had but one eye, one arm, and one leg. When they grew up she told them, "Never fish to the south, only to the west."

When the boys went fishing at the west end of the island, they didn't find any fish.

"So we fish in the other direction," the oldest boy said.

"Mother told us not to," another brother said.

"We haven't caught anything here," the oldest argued.

A third brother said, "Eh, I don't know. Mother said."

"Look, let's just fish, that's all. See if we can catch anything today."

The second said, "Okay, we'll do it, but only because you're the oldest."

They walked to the south end of the island. There they fished, fished, fished, and fished.

Across the reef, on a small island, lived a demon. He saw the boys at the south end of their island. "Wow, I got food coming." The demon pulled up a coconut, sat, and watched as the boys fished, fished, fished, and fished ever closer to his own island.

Now the demon had special fish called **merā**. When the boys got very close, the demon sang to his fish:

> *Lōe im tōtor,*
> *ilo no in lijmōrmōr,*
> *ieō wekare welok eo merā drik eo.*

> You, there, running on the reef's waves,
> there on the whitecaps,
> Stick the fish, stick the *merā* shell.

The fish swam right near the boys. They hopped after the fish. The boys got badly scratched and cut on the reef, so they scrambled to the demon's beach to lie down on the sand.

"Hey, you, *iakwe* to you all," the demon said.

"*Iakwe, iakwe,*" the boys answered, each holding his lone foot.

"What happened there?"

"We got cut on the reef."

"Don't worry, don't worry," the demon said. "Come with me now."

The boys followed the demon. He made a fire under a *kiden* tree. He warmed up a few of the leaves and gave one to each boy. "Wrap a warm leaf on your foot."

When every foot felt better, the demon took the boys to his house. "Jump right in, boys," the demon told them. You see, the demon's house was a big hole in the ground. The boys leapt right in, one after another. When they were all in, the demon called to his **bale** fish:

> *Bale kil mejen roñ ne.*
> Fish, cover the hole.

The fish leapt in, burying the boys. When the boys had all died, the demon ate them.

On Ieb, the mother grew very sad.

Soon she got pregnant again and had twelve more boys. Like their brothers, each had one eye, one arm, and one leg. When they were old enough she told them, "Never fish to the south, only to the west."

The boys fished, fished, fished, and fished along the west side. They caught no fish.

"Let's fish to the south," the oldest boy said.

"But mother told us not to fish that way," another brother said.

"We haven't caught anything here," the oldest argued.

A third brother said, "Okay, you're the oldest."

They fished, fished, fished, and fished all the way to the south end.

The demon saw the boys. "Mmmm, there's a lot of food on the reef."

He pulled up a coconut to watch them. When the boys got very near the reef of his island, the demon sang to his *merā* fish:

> *Lōe im tōtor,*
> *ilo no in lijmōrmōr,*
> *ieō wekare welok eo merā drik eo.*

> You, there, running on the reef's waves,
> there on the whitecaps,
> Stick the fish, stick the *merā* shell.

The boys hopped after the fish. They got scratched and cut. They leapt to the demon's shore.

"Hey you, *iakwe* to you all," the demon said.

"*Iakwe, iakwe.*"

"What are you guys doing here?"

"We hurt ourselves."

"Don't worry, don't worry, you come with me."

They followed the demon to the *kiden* tree, where he fixed their feet with warmed leaves. "Okay, let's go to my place."

The boys followed him to that hole. They jumped in. The demon called to his *bale* fish:

> *Bale kil mejen roñ ne.*
> Fish, cover the hole.

The fish did. The boys died. The demon ate them.

Their mother grew so very sad.

Again she gave birth to twelve boys. But this time the youngest boy had two eyes, two arms, and two legs. His brothers called him Lakkiñ, meaning the youngest whom no one cares about.

Whatever his brothers did, Lakkiñ always asked, "Can I come, too?"

The brothers always answered, "You're not real, Lakkiñ. Stay with mother."

But Lakkiñ kept on asking.

So when the eleven gathered their fishing sticks, Lakkiñ was right there asking. "Please, brothers, can I come, can I come, too?"

"No. You're different. You're no good for us."

This time, the boys' mother stepped in. "He's been asking nicely. Take him with you."

The oldest brother sighed, "Okay, but find your own fishing stick, Lakkiñ."

"Let's go," cried the others.

"Never fish to the south, boys," their mother told them, "only to the west."

Lakkiñ grabbed his mother's *ie* and ran after his brothers.

*ie* [eeay] a large needle used to make mats

The boys fished, fished, fished, and fished, but like the others, they caught no fish.

"To the south," the oldest boy said.

"Mother told us . . . ," Lakkiñ started to say, but the oldest cut him off.

"We haven't caught anything here, you little stupid head."

A third brother said, "Yeah, ugly face, just keep quiet."

The brothers fished, fished, fished, and fished to the south end.

Across the reef, sitting on his coconut, the demon watched. "Oooo, food."

When the boys reached his reef, he sang:

> *Lōe im tōtor,*
> *ilo no in lijmōrmōr,*
> *ieō wekare welok eo merā drik eo.*

> You, there, running on the reef's waves,
> there on the whitecaps,
> Stick the fish, stick the *merā* shell.

The boys hopped after those fish, got scratched and cut and leapt onto the demon's beach. All but the youngest. Lakkiñ kept chasing the fish. He could run the reef without cutting either of his feet.

"*Iakwe* to you all."

"*Iakwe, iakwe.*"

"What are you boys doing?"

"We got hurt."

"Don't worry, don't worry, you come with me."

While the demon fixed each boy's foot, Lakkiñ killed all the *merā*.

He tossed the dead fish onto the beach. The demon was truly surprised. "What kind of person is this?" he thought, but only said, "Come to my house."

All the boys jumped into the hole except Lakkiñ. "You jump in first," he said to the demon.

"No, no, you first," answered the demon.

"It's your house."

"You're the guest."

They argued, argued, and argued until Lakkiñ gave in. "Okay, okay, I'll jump."

The demon called to his *bale*, then hurried off to prepare for his newest meal.

Deep in the hole, the brothers panicked. But Lakkiñ pulled out his mother's *ie* and killed every last fish. "Come on, brothers," he said. "We don't want Mother missing us."

They hopped as fast as a foot could take them. Lakkiñ grabbed a pandanus leaf and tried a little *bubu,* magic.

He asked the leaf, "Should we go to the ocean side?"

With a twirl and a shake, the leaf said no.

"What should we do, Lakkiñ?" the brothers asked, trying to keep up with him.

"How about the middle of the island?" Lakkiñ asked the leaf.

The leaf shivered and gave another no.

Meanwhile the demon returned to the empty hole. "My fish."

"Lakkiñ!" cried his brothers. "Where do we go?"

Lakkiñ twirled the leaf once more. "Lagoon side?"

"Good" was the answer.

The demon began to follow the single line of footprints.

Near the lagoon, there sat a house. "Hide in the ceiling," Lakkiñ cried, and turned the leaf again. "Do I stay with my brothers?"

The leaf gave a no, so Lakkiñ climbed down.

"This is really stupid," the oldest said.

"But we're not dead," another answered.

"He'll get himself killed," said a third.

"Let him go!" exclaimed another. "As long as we're safe."

The demon searched from one end of the island to the other.

Lakkiñ built a fire.

The demon ran from ocean side to lagoon side.

Lakkiñ made the fire burn hot, hot, hot.

Finally, the demon smelled the boys.

*jirul* [jih-RUHL] small shells that look like eyes

Lakkiñ put six rocks in the fire. Lakkiñ picked up two *jirul*. He put the shells over his eyelids and fell asleep.

The demon chanted:

> *Laddrik ra-ra, Laddrik ra-ra,*
> *komij item et,*
> *letok juon kijōr ek ak*
> *letok juon kijōr armij.*

> Boys, boys,
> What are you doing here,
> Give me one fish or give me one human.

Still hiding in the ceiling, the oldest heard the chanting. "Did you hear that?"

"It's just the sound of the wind, right?" another brother said.

The chant repeated.

The boys were really scared.

The demon saw the light of the fire. He moved very slowly, chanting the whole way.

The boys upstairs were so scared, they peed their pants.

The demon chanted again.

*Laddrik ra-ra, Laddrik ra-ra,*
*komij item et,*
*letok juon kijōr ek ak*
*letok juon kijōr armij.*

Boys, boys,
What are you doing here,
Give me one fish or give me one human.

Lakkiñ woke up and called, "Here's a fish!" He tossed a hot rock. The demon bit it right out of the air and swallowed the rock.

He sang again, and Lakkiñ threw another rock. The demon sang on and on, swallowing rock after rock till he died.

Lakkiñ called to his brothers. Some had passed out and some had messed all over themselves they were so scared. He woke them all up and took them back to a very happy mother.

*So don't let the youngest down; some day he will help you. Listen and show* iakwe. *That's the end of the story.*

# RI-JORAN, THE BAD PERSON

***ri-joran***
[ree-joh-RAHN]
a bad person

*The title of this story, which is about a bad person, is "Ri-Joran." We have customs and beliefs that are very important, and this story tells you about these. Like sometimes after a person died, that person would visit the living, like in dreams. This happened once to a woman.*

On an island there was hardly any food. A man died, leaving his wife and son alone. Every, every, every day the woman looked for food, but she hardly found enough to keep even a bird alive. And she never had a chance to rest. Her son was too young to help.

One night the boy was so very hungry, he cried. The woman could hardly keep her eyes open. "You have to be strong," she told her son. "I need to sleep for a little while."

"Okay, mother," the boy said, wiping away his tears. "Take a little rest."

*Now this is what I'm telling you about.*

The woman felt tired because her dead husband was calling to her. It made her sleepy. When she had fallen completely asleep, the man appeared to her.

"Tomorrow morning," the man said, "dig a hole in front of your window. After you finish, pick a palm frond. Throw the leaves away, but keep the stem. Then, collect the bark of the **armwe** tree. Tie a strip of the bark to the end of the palm stem to make a fishing pole. Give the boy the fishing pole, and tell him to lower it into the hole and chant like this:

*armwe*
AHRM-weh

> *Lieo jo eo ielen lōklōk lu-ji-kue,*
> *kuban luj aded ne*
> *ñim kōme luj aded ne*
> *ñim aded eo ñin jinerro in.*

Boy, bring food from inside the shell for me and for you and for your mother to eat.

As the chant finished, the woman woke up. She sat for a while, thinking, "Is this really true? My husband talking to me? Is it true what he told me?"

The woman woke her son. Together they did as her husband told her. As they chanted, the boy lowered the fishing pole into the hole. When they finished chanting, the boy lifted the fishing pole. A big basket of pumpkin mixed with flour hung at the end of the bark.

The boy called, "Mother! See what I caught!"

The woman leaned out the window to take a closer look. "Son, this is good luck for us, this delicious food."

"Oh, I didn't know this was luck," the boy said.

"Just throw your fishing pole again."

So the boy lowered it again and chanted:

> *Lieo jo eo ielen lōklōk lu-ji-kue,*
> *kuban luj aded ne*
> *ñim kōme luj aded ne*
> *ñim aded eo ñin jinerro in.*

Boy, bring food from inside the shell for me
and for you and for your mother to eat.

He pulled the fishing pole up, up, up, up, and
up. This time he caught a basket of chicken. He was
really wondering at this. "Mother, look what's
inside this one."

"Don't you see?" she told him, "This is the meat
for the pumpkin."

The boy chanted a third time. He brought up a
basket of coconuts so big he could hardly even drink
one. "Mother?"

"Son, this is for us to drink, so you can stop fishing. We can eat now."

They ate, ate, ate, and ate, more than they had
ever eaten. The mother told her boy, "Son, we must
**ejtōbtōb** now."

"What's that?"

"*Ejtōbtōb* is a custom you must know," she said.

"If you eat good food and don't share with the
others of the island, then you'll always stay hungry.
But first, we give some to the *iroij*."

They gathered some of the food into a special
basket and headed off for the *iroij*'s house.
When they arrived, the old woman said, "**Iakwe
komi**."

"**Kom emmol**," the *iroij* answered.

"We have a little something for you and all the
people of your house."

The woman and her son laid the basket near the
*iroij*.

He was so surprised. "Where's all this food from?
This island has no food."

"We're just lucky, I guess," the little boy said,
and together, he and his mother turned for home.

**ejtōbtōb**
[EJ-teuhb-teuhb]
a custom that
states that if
people eat good
food and don't
share with oth-
ers, they will
remain hungry

**iakwe komi**
[ee-ah-KWEH
keh-MEE]
greetings

**kom emmol**
[kohm em-
MOHL]
thank you (to
several people)

*Now by this time you're wondering about the title of this story, "the bad people." Well, it's coming. You see . . .*

The same thing went on every day after that. The boy took the fishing pole, threw it into the hole, and chanted. Every time plenty of food came out.

The woman knew they needed to share more food with the people of their island. That's the custom we call **bidrikdrik maroñroñ** —if you have something, even if it's little, you have to share with other people.

The woman asked her son to fish out a big supply of food. Three big baskets of coconut came first, followed by three baskets of pumpkin, and three different types of breadfruit, one raw, one cooked, and one mixed with coconut oil. Next he reeled in three big baskets of fish. The boy grew tired from all that fishing, so his mother told him, "That's good enough. Come eat with me."

That night, after the boy and his mother fed all the people on the island, the boy fished again. Nearby hid another boy, the *ri-joran*, peeking. Ri-Joran listened as the boy chanted. He watched as the boy pulled three baskets of food for dinner.

After they fell asleep, Ri-Joran came out of hiding. He took the fishing pole and chanted quietly. Ri-Joran brought up a basket of reef fish. But he didn't stop there. He fished, fished, fished, and fished, all kinds of food he fished, baskets and baskets of food. When he finished, he broke the fishing pole, just threw it away. He took the baskets and left before anyone knew. And Ri-Joran never shared the food.

*So what happened? Because of Ri-Joran, the bad boy, the people didn't have enough food. When*

**bidrikdrik maroñroñ**
[BIH-rihk-rihk MAH-rohng-rohng]
a custom that states that if you have something, even if it's little, you should share it with other people

*there's a* ri-joran, *bad things happen to us. That's why the title of this story.*

# UNDERGROUND PEOPLE

*The people from under the ground, they're powerful. This story tells you about an island of underground people and really good fishing.*

A demon lived on an island of good fishing, but he always felt hungry because no people ever came around. He grumbled about that. His stomach growled because of that.

Under that island of good fishing lived some people. They liked fish. They got hungry too. So three underground boys, **Lubale**, **Lōbetaña**, and **Lobaia**, the youngest, came up through the demon's well to fish.

The demon was building a new house. He paused. "I smell people." He went searching for the smell. On the ocean side he saw the boys fishing at a place called **Bōkbōk**. He hid in the bushes and sang to them.

> *Lobale, Lobale, Lōbetaña, Lobaia, am bolii-wa*
> *Lobale, Lobale, Lōbetaña, Lobaia, Raaaaaaa!*

"Hey brothers!" the youngest said, "Did you hear that sound?"

> *Lobale, Lobale, Lōbetaña, Lobaia, am bolii-wa*
> Lobale, Lobale, Lōbetaña, Lobaia, Raaaaaaa!

**Lubale**
loo-BAH-leh

**Lōbetaña** leuh-bay-tah-NGA

**Lobaia** loh-BAH-ee-ah

**Bōkbōk**
BEUHK-beuhk

"Brothers," Lobaia cried again, "what's that sound?"

"We don't hear anything," the others answered. "Just keep fishing."

*Lobale, Lobale, Lōbetaña, Lobaia, am bolii-wa*
*Lobale, Lobale, Lōbetaña, Lobaia, Raaaaaaa!*

"No, no," Lobaia insisted, "listen!"

"What is this craziness?" the oldest, Lobale, said. "We're trying to fish."

"You have to listen."

The older brothers stopped. The demon stopped. Lōbetaña laughed. "It's just the wind."

Lobale and Lōbetaña went back to fishing, and the demon sang again.

*Lobale, Lobale, Lōbetaña, Lobaia, am bolii-wa*
Lobale, Lobale, Lōbetaña, Lobaia, Raaaaaaa!

"See? See?" Lobaia was nearly screaming, "There!"

The demon leapt out. The boys dropped their poles. The demon tried to chomp them, but the boys disappeared into the bushes. He never saw them jump into his well.

"Raaaaaa!" the demon cried, and stamped off to his new house. He fell asleep, hungry.

In the morning, the boys returned. They gathered their poles and fished again. The demon woke up to their smell. He ran quickly to the fishing spot.

*Lobale, Lobale, Lōbetaña, Lobaia, am bolii-wa*
*Lobale, Lobale, Lōbetaña, Lobaia, Raaaaaaa!*

"There it is." Lobaia said, trembling. "There's that sound again!"

"Quiet," said Lobale. "Follow me." The younger brothers followed. Lobale walked very slowly.

The demon followed slowly.

"He's there. He's there!" cried the youngest.

"Quiet!" whispered Lōbetaña.

"Run!" yelled the oldest. They ran straight for the demon's well.

The demon stayed close, but as he reached out to grab them, the brothers disappeared. This time the demon caught sight of Lobaia's head disappearing into the ground. "Ah, now I know."

The demon didn't sleep that night. He worked till the sun rose. He worked until he smelled those boys once again. When he smelled that smell, the demon grabbed the big net he had made and went to the well. The demon watched as the boys climbed out. He laughed quietly as the boys went off to the fishing place. He covered the well with the net.

*Lobale, Lobale, Lōbetaña, Lobaia, am bolii-wa*
Lobale, Lobale, Lōbetaña, Lobaia, Raaaaaaa!

"It's him!" the youngest shouted. "The demon's here!"

"You don't need to make so much noise," the oldest said. "Just run."

They ran. They jumped into the well. The demon gathered up the net and boys. "Now I get to eat."

The demon hung the brothers in a tree as he gathered sticks and rocks to build an *um*, an underground oven.

"He's going to cook us!" the youngest cried.

"Never mind that," Lobale said, "Bite down on this."

Lobaia bit the net. His brothers joined him. They bit and bit and bit until the net broke open and they tumbled to the ground. The demon came running. Lobale and Lōbetaña disappeared into the well, but the demon caught Lobaia. "Brothers!" he cried, but they were long gone. The youngest had to fight.

From lagoonside to oceanside, Lobaia and the demon fought. From oceanside to lagoonside, the demon was winning. But as they fought back to oceanside, Lobaia came out on top. He tied the demon up in his own net.

Lobale and Lōbetaña leapt out of the well. The brothers tossed the demon into his newly built home and burned it to the ground, demon and all.

*I know this happened because I helped the boys do it. Then we all fished.*

# LETAO BRINGS FIRE

*[Jackning took me on a tour of Japanese World War II ruins on Tarawa, Maloelap. At one big hole in the ground, he mentioned that the Americans had blown up a very large supply building. The information as to the location of the building had been leaked by a local clergyman. The clergyman had his head cut off by the Japanese military. This brief anecdote made Jackning think of Letao, and as we walked back to our house, he told this story.]*

Letao was sailing from the Ralik chain of islands to the Ratak chain of islands. He stopped at Likiep. There, he saw some Likiep men fishing. Letao approached one of the men and asked for a fishing pole. The man said, "Get your own."

Letao turned all of them into trees.

As he walked on, Letao came across some boys who were on their way to fish. Letao asked the boys for a fishing pole. "I hear it's good fishing in Likiep."

The smallest boy gave Letao a pole. Letao fished up plenty of fish. He shared it with the little boy.

"*Jij*!" said the boy.

*jij* jihj

"This is what you get when you share," answered Letao.

The boy started eating the fish right away, but Letao stopped him. "Do you like eating your fish cold or would you like it cooked?"

"Cooked?" asked the boy. "What's 'cooked'?"

Letao struck up a fire. The boy nearly ran away.

"Wait!" shouted Letao. "Try this."

Letao cooked the fish and gave one to the boy. He was scared to try. So Letao ate first. Then the boy tried the cooked fish.

"*Jij*!" said the boy.

"So which is better?" asked Letao. "The cold or the cooked?"

"Cooked."

"Then go on home, and you'll have fire," said Letao.

The boy ran home as quickly as he could. When he got there, his house was on fire.

"Cooked! Cooked house!" shouted the boy.

But then, suddenly, it wasn't.

"Now you know fire," said Letao and got into his canoe and sailed off.

And Letao sailed to America, and that's why the people there are so smart.

# RATAK CHAIN *Sunrise Islands*
# ARNO

# ARNO

## LAKILMEJ LINE

**Lakilmej Line**
lah-KIHL-mej
leyen

Every so often, when telling stories of his own life, Lakilmej Line would burst into laughter. He told me other people don't believe him. He added, "People still ask me, when you go fishing do you use black magic? You catch so many fish!" And another laugh burst out of him.

Lakilmej Line is from Arno. He grew up there with his grandparents because his father went off to work with the Japanese during the war. He says, "My grandfather taught me how to fish from the time I could speak. [burst of laughter] I went out with my grandfather from morning until night on the canoe. He taught me how to look at fish and tell which is poisonous. But when I tell other people, they don't believe me!" [burst of laughter]

Lakilmej relishes the story of one such man who caught a big fish. The man asked if anyone wanted it. Lakilmej asked what kind of fish it was and the man told him a ***nitwa***. Lakilmej laughed and said, "It isn't. Just look in its mouth." He said he turned to the other people there. "I told them to throw out the fish they brought. They argued with me, but then everyone threw the fish away." [burst of laughter]

*nitwa* NIHT-wah

Lakilmej says he doesn't have anyone to teach his special fishing skills to, as his son is a carpenter, plumber, and electrician. So, to date, he hasn't passed his knowledge on.

# MAGIC FISHING AND WHALE CRIES

## Magic Fishing

I was brought up by my grandfather from when I was a year old, so I thought he was my father. My daddy [grandfather] was really a fisherman. You know, any kind of fishing he could do. When everyone went fishing, my daddy was always the leader. I always rode in his canoe, and he told me, "You watch me and then you're going to do it." He taught me magic to catch fish. My daddy told me if I used the magic wrong then nothing would happen. Nothing.

Mostly then, everyone knew how to do it. Now, in these days, they don't know how to do it. They don't know the tides. If you're not with the right tide, you don't catch anything.

I only used the magic my grandfather taught me three times. The first time I was going to school. After three months at the school one teacher called me. He took me out of class and told me to go catch some fish. He put me in charge of five boys. I was the oldest and I could speak broken English. The other boys couldn't talk with some of the teachers, because so many teachers were American.

We went to the lagoon. I asked one of the boys to climb the coconut tree. He asked, "Why do you ask that?"

"We're going to make a trap," I told them, "a magic trap for fish."

One of them said, "That's a lie." The others, they believed me. "We'll try our best," they said. We got some coconut leaves and wove them together. Then we built the trap in the water with the leaves and rocks. When we did this, they asked me, "When do we catch the fish?"

"Three days," I said. "Wait three days and if there's nothing, then there's nothing."

Thursday, Friday, and Saturday passed. Sunday morning I went to look. I climbed the coconut tree. I saw the trap. A lot of fish were inside. I watched some big fish pushing their way in to get at the little fish. I took a coconut leaf to cover the opening. But since it wasn't low tide yet, I went back to my room and slept.

The boys of the school were cooking up a lot of food. Someone had forgotten to clean out the big cooking tub. Two of them took the tub to the lagoon to clean it. They saw my trap and all the fish. Since it was already low tide, the fish were dead. Those two boys dropped the tub and came running and told everyone about the fish.

The boys came running to me. "There's so many fish!"

"I already know," I told them. I got up and went back to the lagoon.

When the principal saw all the fish in the trap, he was surprised. "Next week, I'm going to get all the boys to get the rocks to bring them here." Nowadays you can still see the rocks on that side for my trap.

The American teacher asked me, "How did you do that?"

I told him but he said, "I don't believe it."

When my grandfather taught me I told him, "I don't believe it." But I learned it. And there's never been so many fish in that lagoon from that time to now.

## Magic Fishing, Part 2

After we ate breakfast, we walked back to the lagoon. One boy wanted to see the magic. I gave him a special-made coconut leaf. I showed him how to drag it near the top of the water. When we dragged it to shore, it was really full of fish. That boy said, "Wow! How did that happen?"

"Why, you know, I don't know. I just know the fish don't go under the leaf trap."

When he counted the fish, we had ninety-nine.

I told him, "Well, I'm going to separate the fish. Some for me, some for you, some for the other boys."

"How come you give me this?" he asked me.

"That's the custom. You give some to your family. Since we are here together, this is like my family."

Today it's hard to get people together like that. Today all the boys, they all think they're so smart. They don't want to listen to someone, anyone. Not like before. Everyone worked together, fished together, shared together. Family was important, and so was the custom. I don't know what to do about it.

## Whale Cries

Let me tell you about the big fish, like the, how you call it? whale. You've heard of the whale fishing? It's really funny, that kind. When we bring a whale to the shore, the whale cries like a baby. Yeah, they cry, wow! Last time I helped catch a whale was in Arno. Maybe about 1950.

The chief called everybody because a whale got

stuck in the lagoon, couldn't find its way out. He stayed in the Arno lagoon for maybe three, maybe four months. The chief called everyone to bring their canoes. Each canoe had two to four men on board. Two men were the fishers and two men paddled. The fishermen carried rocks.

As they watched the whale, one man dived. Under the water the man knocked the rocks together. He kept knocking till he had to come up to breathe, and then the other fisherman dived. He knocked rocks together, too. After all the knocking, the whale leapt up out of the water. Every time the whale went back under the water, the men dived and knocked the rocks to bring it back up. They steered the whale close to the shore.

When the whale got to shore, that big fish cried. Wow! How come this one do that? Maybe it's really a human being! They cry so much like people. That time in Arno, that was the second time I heard the big fish cry. My first time I was too young. I watched from the shore. This time I was diving and hitting the rocks. Really funny, that kind of fishing.

## Magic Fishing, Part 3

Another time I used the magic was on Mili. I went there with my cousin. The government sent us to clean up the island after the war. I went as the mechanic.

When I reached there, my cousin told me, "Why don't you go to the small island and make copra for some money."

When I got to the small island, I saw a lot of fish near the shore, the kind good for sashimi. I told the other men, "Eh! Let's stop and get those."

Those men laughed at me and said, "From the time the oldest man was here, nobody could ever catch these fish. They're smart. Those fish don't want to get caught. Soon as you get near, they run away."

I don't know, maybe there's a thousand fish. I picked up one rock. I threw it and as soon as it hit, they swam away. Not even ten minutes passed and they came back. I threw another rock and they ran away. But I saw they swam to the same place. I laughed and said to those men, "I can catch them."

They didn't believe me. They went off to make copra. Me, I waited until low tide. I waded out and made a semicircle with rocks facing to the shore. The men making copra were mad at me: "Why isn't he helping? He just goes fishing!"

When I finished with the rocks, the tide came up. I left a spot open in the rock circle so the fish could come in. I stood inside the circle and threw rocks near the fish. All of them swam really fast, right into the rock circle! I just stood there and laughed. I closed the circle, then threw more rocks. The fish had nowhere to go. They swam straight to the shore. Some jumped up on the shore and died. I yelled to the men, "Bring your spears. Take what you like!" I laughed so much, at the fish and the men. Wow! So many fish they got that day!

Even today, if you go to Mili, you can see my trap. I told my cousin after, "Well, this trap is yours now. I'm not going to be back. Maybe you can use it."

**The Pearl Hook**

When I was little, my grandfather took me out fishing with an old man. My grandfather said, "This man really knows how to fish." The other men, they didn't believe it. He was just a weak old man, they said. Those men in the boat with us, they put their fishing line in for a long time. We sailed, and they dragged their fishing line behind us, trolling. By the time we got to the channel, the men were tired. "Bring the lines into the boat," they said to each other.

The old man grabbed his line and threw it in then, just when the other men took their lines out. The old man chanted while switching the line back and forth between his hands. Three or four times he bent forward. The men were surprised. They didn't know what to make of this old man's ways.

The old man tried to sit back up, but he could hardly pull his line up. The other men had to help. Wow! What a big fish they pulled up, and so fast. And my grandfather and the old man, they just talked story the whole time, like it wasn't so special.

The old man had a special kind of hook made from pearl. I had one, too, that he gave me, but when I was working in Kwajalein, someone stole it.

My grandfather said if you troll with that hook, no other boats will catch anything. I don't know, I never got to try it. It was beautiful, that hook, really shined. But I don't know who can make it anymore. No one paid attention to that old man so they didn't learn from him.

# MILI

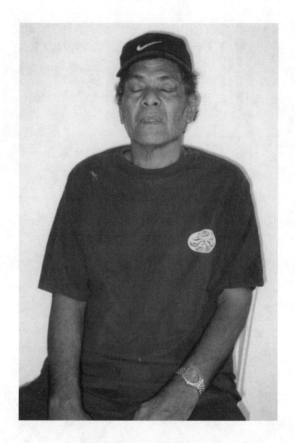

## MEJIN JITIAM

In the early 1990s Mejin Jitiam was chosen to go to Hawai'i to study star navigation with navigators from all over the Pacific in preparation for the 1992 Pacific Arts Festival. He spent a month there. "I liked being in Hawai'i because we (the navigators) learned from each other. Also, Hawai'i has a different kind of boat from the Marshalls, with a wheel to steer."

Mejin and another navigator named Toshiro were among a small group that represented the Marshall Islands at the festival in Rarotonga. A day was set aside for traditional canoes from all over the Pacific to sail between two islands. However, Mejin's daughter got very sick, so he had to return home before the big event.

It was his grandfather who first taught navigation. He was the only boy in his famil learned. His grandfather gave him the responsi of teaching his brothers. For the first year o training, they sailed only inside the lagoon. Thei the second year, they sailed between islands, fr Mili to Majuro and Jaluit.

Mejin is now teaching navigation to the son Mili's senator.

Mejin's family is from Likiep and Mili. His grandfather was an *iroij* from Mili. His *joui* is **Ri-Jaluit**.

**Ri-Jaluit**
ree-JA-loo-iht

**MEJIN JITIAM**

# HALF-BOY AND THE DOG

**Jelkwon**
JEL-kwohn

*I don't know if you've heard this story yet. About the breadfruit? This breadfruit I'm talking about belonged to a dog on an island called **Jelkwon**. It was delicious, the most delicious breadfruit. Everyone knew that, but the dog let no one get it.*

**Lukonwor**
LUH-kohn-wohr

On another island, called **Lukonwor**, six boys lived with their parents. The old lady and old man asked, "Who is going to bring the breadfruit from Jelkwon? We are so scared of the dog that lives there."

The youngest boy said, "Me. I'll bring it."

"Ha!" his brothers laughed. "You? What are you going to do?"

*The youngest of the brothers, he was different. He had only one eye, one ear, one leg, and one arm. Everything that should be two was only one. He was only half a boy.*

The five older brothers loaded up their canoe and sailed off without him.

When the boys neared Jelkwon Island, the dog leapt out from the bushes, threatening them. "Leave my island," it barked at them. "Leave my breadfruit!"

The boys sailed quickly back home, without even a single breadfruit.

When the next day dawned, the old people felt

really hungry for those breadfruit. "Who can bring them?" they asked.

The youngest spoke up quickly, "Me. Me."

"Ha!" his brothers laughed.

"Ha, to you," said their parents. "You brought nothing. Take your younger brother with you."

So the boys sailed, this time with their half-brother.

At Jelkwon, before the boys even stopped the canoe, the half-boy grabbed a basket and hopped off.

"Watch for the dog!" his brothers shouted.

As he was only half a boy, though, the dog didn't see him. The dog barked and threatened his older brothers in the canoe while half-boy picked the breadfruit. When he had filled the basket, half-boy slipped easily past the dog, and the brothers all sailed back to Lukonwor.

"We got a lot of the breadfruit," the oldest shouted as they landed on the shore. "So many breadfruit. The island is full, just full, of that delicious breadfruit."

The family ate and ate and ate. They ate that delicious breadfruit till it was gone. The parents were so pleased with their oldest son, the next day they told him to go again. "You proved you aren't afraid of that dog, son."

The brothers sailed.

"Here I go," called half-boy, but his oldest brother grabbed him.

"Oh, no," he said. "Mama and papa asked me to go."

The oldest walked onto the island. The dog grabbed him and sliced him into pieces. The other brothers ran to help, but the dog sliced them, too. Half-boy pushed the canoe into the ocean and sailed home.

"All my brothers died," he told his parents. "The dog ate them."

"What will we do now?" the old lady asked.

Half-boy said, "I'll go and bring a branch of the breadfruit. Then we won't need to go back there anymore."

He sailed to Jelkwon, hopped passed the dog without even disturbing it, stole a branch, and sailed home. Half-boy and his parents had plenty of the delicious breadfruit from that day on.

*If you go there you'll see the breadfruit. I've eaten some of it and it is, it's delicious. We eat from that breadfruit now. And now we've got a lot of breadfruit from the one that the half-boy stole.*

*The dog is gone.*

# ARBAR

## ROSE JOHNSON

I hired a small boat to get to Arbar Island to visit Rose Johnson. Over eighty years old, she had agreed (by radio through her son) to share stories with me. We went at low tide, which meant we had to walk through part of the lagoon to get to Arbar. The lagoon was full of sea slugs.

Arbar is a big, long island, crammed full of trees. There are very few houses. So few people live there, in fact, the "main road" is a skinny path along the lagoon side of the island. There are no toilets.

Rose lives in a small, wooden house. She sleeps in the "backroom," a small, partitioned-off section of the house, the whole of which is about the size of a small American living room.

**Arbar** AHR-bahr

Lok lohk

Ris rihj

Narlo NAHR-loh

Nadrikdrik
  NAH-rihk-rihk

Rose's family is from the various islands of Mili. Her *joui* on her father's side is **Lok**; on her mother's, **Ris**. She was the oldest girl in a family of twelve children. Born on **Narlo** Island, Rose was adopted by a family relative and grew up on the island of **Nadrikdrik**. When she returned at age seventeen, her family had a big birthday party for her.

The Japanese arrived in Mili when she was around twenty years old. She remembers having to carry sand and rocks and dig holes for hiding during bombing raids. "They made us work like slaves. All the men and women had to work, cooking salt water for salt as well as making food for them."

When the Americans came, she and her family swam out to the boats. "The Japanese were shooting at us. I was scared because my baby sister had just been born. My father swam with the baby's mouth inside his to get to the boat."

As she told me stories, Rose sat in her room, half invisible to me because of the plywood partition. Just past her I could see a shelf that held the wealth of her personal items: a Bible, a *lei* of flowers, a small container of powered Kool-aid and a can of Sterno.

Throughout her tellings, she slapped at flies buzzing through the house. You can hear the regular rhythm of her fan banging against her legs on my tapes of her.

ROSE JOHNSON

# AKŪT WOMAN

*This story is about an old woman, living in a village called* **Monebbort***.*

This old lady, she didn't do any kind of work. She was lazy. The only thing she did was *akūt*, look for lice on her head.

Every day she woke up feeling hungry. But she never cooked for herself. Every day she just wandered to the big rock near the village and sat doing *akūt*.

The people of her village passed by her every day, watching her, staring at her, but she ignored them. *Akūt, akūt, akūt.* All day she did nothing but *akūt* there on the rock, ignoring everyone around her. The people made fun of her, "Hey, look at that old woman there just doing the *akūt, akūt, akūt*." But that lazy old woman paid no attention. *Akūt, akūt, akūt.* Just *akūt, akūt, akūt*.

She never did work and she never ate, except the lice she found as she did the *akūt*.

One day she went to the rock so very, very hungry. As she did her *akūt*, she died.

*We have this story to make us remember not to be so lazy.*

*akūt* (also *ekit*)
 [EH-kiht]
 to look for lice

**Monebbort**
 MOH-neb-bohrt

Rose Johnson

# THE BEAUTIFUL WOMAN, THE UGLY MAN

*The* leroij *of Mili are beautiful. But if one has a husband, he is ugly. It came down from this story.*

**Likjor** LIHK-johr

**Likinmōrlik**
lih-kihn-
MEUHR-lihk

**Lañelinwōd**
lahng-el-IHN-
weuhr

A *leroij* named **Likjor** lived on Mili Island in the village of **Likinmōrlik**. Her beauty made her famous all over Mili Atoll.

One *iroij*, **Lañelinwōd**, heard everyone talking about her. He told his men to make ready his canoe. One man made the *ujela* (sail), one navigated, several paddled the canoe, one bailed the water, and one man had the job of tying the anchor to the reef. This last man, they called him **Kweat** because he really knew how to make the anchor hold tight to the reef, just like an octopus. They also called him Kweat because he was as ugly as an octopus.

**Kweat** [KWAY-eht] octopus or squid

When Lañelinwōd's canoes appeared on the horizon, *Leroij* Likjor told all the women to clean their hair, douse themselves with perfume, and gather at the shore.

It was dark by the time Lañelinwōd and his men landed. Even though the Likinmōrlik women brought firesticks, they could hardly see the men's faces. The men leapt out of their canoes and each took one woman for himself.

*Iroij* Lañelinwōd was the last to leave. He called

out to the woman tending the fire outside the village. "Turn off the fire. The **koonwadrik** is coming now."

The woman doused the fire. The *iroij* ducked into the house of the *leroij*. He spent a long time there.

Kweat, the ugly one, finished tying up the canoes. He walked alone to the village. The fire outside the village burned bright, so Kweat called out, "Turn off the fire. The *koonwadrik* is coming now."

The lady kicked out the fire, saying, "Are there a lot of *koonwadrik* coming from over there?"

Kweat ignored her and ducked into the first house he came to. It was the house of the *leroij*. As the real *iroij* stepped out the back of the house, Kweat pulled up the mat *Leroij* Likjor was sleeping under and crawled in.

*Iroij* Lañelinwōd walked the village, waking his men. "Time to sail."

They returned to the canoes, but Kweat was nowhere to be seen. *Iroij* Lañelinwōd told a couple of men, "Go find and wake the ugly one. He needs to untie the boats."

The men heard Kweat sleeping deeply. When they tried to wake him, however, they had a hard time. They pushed him and kicked him; they pushed him and pulled him. Nothing worked. Kweat, being so like an octopus, was well stuck to the mat. Finally, one of the men just kicked him. Kweat woke with a start. The men went off to get their canoes ready.

"He's coming," they told the *iroij*.

Kweat slowly unstuck himself from the mat.

The men and the *iroij* sat and waited in their canoes.

*koonwadrik*
[keuhn-WAH-rihk]
an old word for *iroij,* or chief

Kweat woke the *leroij*. "We need to say goodbye to each other."

The *iroij* ordered his men to cut the canoes loose.

The *leroij* awoke, took one look at the ugly man and threw up.

The *iroij* and his men sailed off.

The *leroij* ran out of her house just as the *iroij*'s canoes disappeared from sight. "No, wait! Take me with you!" *Leroij* Likjor yelled.

Kweat stepped out of the *leroij*'s house. "Don't feel scared," he told her. "It's all right that you were sleeping on my hand. I'm not mad."

The *leroij* screamed and threw up. She ran from island to island trying to catch up with the *iroij*, but Kweat ran close behind, trying to make her feel better. When the *leroij* saw the ugly man coming closer, she threw up again.

She ran and ran and ran, yelling for the *iroij* all the way. The ugly man kept following her, trying to make her feel all right. She kept throwing up.

At the last island, Nallo, *Leroij* Likjor was so exhausted she fell down and died. Kweat went back and lived at her house.

# UJAE

## NITWA JEIK

Ujae OO-jeye

Nitwa Jeik
NIHT-wah jayk

Nitwa Jeik shared his stories on the front walkway of the school where the Ujae mayor had put me up. He told eleven stories within two days, as he was getting ready to leave on the field boat. He finished his final one just before he boarded.

Nitwa can't share the stories he knows unless the *iroij* gives him permission, which he did in my case. On the morning he told me stories, some of the men of the island sat in the distance watching. Later they asked Nitwa what he was doing. Nitwa told them a story he had told me. The men, even though they had lived with Nitwa most of their lives, had never heard the story.

Born on Namdrik, he moved to Ujae when he

was one or two years old. He's lived there ever since. His father taught him to fish and how to build canoes and houses. As a boy he liked to play *riwōt*. His parents always wanted him, not his brothers, to do the work around the house. His brothers were always off playing, and Nitwa never knew why.

His parents taught him how to talk to the *iroij* and how to behave when around the *iroij*. No screaming or whistling, no peeking from behind trees. Children were never to go behind the elders. When Nitwa was young, the *iroij* visited about every three months from Kwajelein and Aeloñlaplap on the boat called *Radio*.

Nitwa started learning stories when he was thirteen. He was taught by two old men, **Latoña**, a Marshallese navigator, and **Rubin**, both relatives of his mother. His mother first took him and his brothers to listen to the stories. Nitwa still doesn't know why. His brothers never hung around much. While he was learning stories, if someone came by, the old men would stop. The next day they'd start up again where they left off.

I asked him if he was afraid the stories will be forgotten. He told me he plans to tell them to his son and added, as he pointed to my tape recorder, "You're recording them now." That kept me laughing for a while.

*riwōt* [REE-weuht] a game named for a toy canoe

**Latoña** lah-TOHNG-ah

**Rubin** ROO-bihn

# TWO DEMON GIRLS OF UJAE

**Rongerik**
ROHNG-eh-rihk

*kiō* KEE-euh

The *iroij* of **Rongerik** Atoll owned a tree, the *kiō*, with the most beautiful yellow flowers. Every morning his flower pickers draped the flowers about his head and neck. The people of Rongerik danced as the flowers were placed on him.

Not far from Rongerik Atoll is the atoll of Ujae, an island of demons. One morning, two demon sisters from Ujae smelled the beauty of the flowers. Their desire for the beauty grew, until one night the two flew to Rongerik Atoll.

The demon girls chanted as they draped themselves with the *iroij*'s *kiō*:

> *Bitbit bitbit waj ikeo jab ne,*
> *ña ikieo jab ie, drieō, drieō belu belu,*
> *belu jenro bik-kelok, kelok jok.*

> Beauty collected in woven baskets,
> We hook flowers behind our ears.
> Decorating each other,
> We fly, fly far away.

When the new morning dawned on Rongerik, the people danced. But the *iroij* flew into a rage. His flowers were gone. He ordered the flower pickers to be killed.

For each of three nights the Ujae sisters flew to the *iroij*'s beautiful tree. For each of three mornings the *iroij* killed his flower pickers for not delivering his precious flowers.

On the fourth morning **Bwilbilinlokerem**, the *iroij*'s assistant, pleaded with him to stop the killing. "Someone must be stealing your flowers. Let me try to catch them tonight."

**Bwilbilinlokerem**
bwihl-bwihl-
ihn-LOH-ker-em

That very night Bwilbilinlokerem took several men and hid by the tree. Just as they were nodding off to sleep, they heard the demon girls' chant:

*Bitbit bitbit waj ikeo jab ne,*
*ña ikieo jab ie, drieō, drieō belu belu,*
*belu jenro bik-kelok, kelok jok.*

Beauty collected in woven baskets,
We hook flowers behind our ears.
Decorating each other,
We fly, fly far away.

As the Ujae sisters leapt away from the tree, the men grabbed them. They hauled the demon girls to the *iroij*'s house.

The *iroij* didn't even bother to look at the two of them as he ordered Bwilbilinlokerem to kill them. The men dragged the sisters away. "Let us go, *iroij*," the demon girls cried out. "We will go straight home and never come back."

The *iroij* glanced down at them. "Stop," he told his men, and then turned to the two. "You are very beautiful." Touching each girl tenderly on the cheek, he continued, "Instead of killing you, I'll take you as my wives."

A great wedding ceremony was held. The people of Rongerik welcomed the girls to the clan. From that day forth the sisters lived with the *iroij* as wives, and the *iroij* once again got his morning flowers.

In time, however, the girls missed their parents. They begged to return, but the *iroij* refused to let them go. The girls persisted, promising to return. The *iroij* finally relented. He ordered a canoe made ready. Together, he and the girls sailed to Ujae. They landed near the place called Menkaru.

The oldest of the girls flew off immediately as they landed. The *iroij* grabbed the younger one and held tight. He ordered the men to go and search for his other wife. He, his young wife, and Bwilbilinlokerem went off to find the demon parents.

The demon people crept out of the bushes as the Rongerik group left. They pulled the *iroij*'s canoe onto the shore. They took it apart and buried it, piece by piece, in the sand.

"We'll catch them and we'll eat them," the demon leader told his people. "We'll cook them with breadfruit and taro."

The demons danced about and sang their demon song. They sang to alert the demons in the nearby islands.

The *iroij*'s company couldn't find the older girl or the parents. They returned to the beach and couldn't find the *iroij*'s canoe either.

"What did you do with it?" the *iroij* yelled at Bwilbilinlokerem.

"We left it . . . , " he tried to answer, but was interrupted by a sound.

**Kaibad**
KEYE-bahr

***Kaibad** O Kaibad,"* the demons sang to each other, gathering for their feast.

The *iroij*'s men jumped. "What's there in the bushes?"

"*Kaibad O Kaibad,*" the demons kept singing. Drums rumbled beneath the call.

"That's my family," the young girl told the chief.

"What do we do?" asked the *iroij*.

The young wife called to a *karuk*, a tiny crab.

> *Rumlok rumlok jako.*
> *Malok malok jako.*

> Dig, dig into the sand.
> Find what's hidden there.

"*Kaibad O Kaibad,*" the demons sang to each other, gathering for their feast.

"*Kaibad O Kaibad*" echoed under her chant. The demons gathered beyond the bushes.

The *karuk* dug up one part of the canoe. The girl called to it again.

> *Rumlok rumlok jako.*
> *Malok malok jako.*

> Dig, dig into the sand.
> Find what's hidden there.

"*Kaibad O Kaibad*," grew in strength and numbers. The men saw shadows of the demons dancing in the bushes.

The *karuk* dug quickly, bringing up different parts of the canoe. As it dug, the men built it again.

"*Kaibad O Kaibad*," sang the demons, as they gathered at the edge of the jungle carrying baskets of taro and breadfruit.

*wut ilomar*
[WOOT ee-loh-MAHR]
a shrub and tree with very large, round leaves used to cover food

The canoe was finished. The demon girl told the *iroij*'s men to bring two long sticks from the **wut ilomar**, a special tree.

The demons stepped from the bushes. The men threw the branches into the canoe. They set sail. The girl took the sticks and stood at the front of the canoe.

The demons leapt into the water, swimming after the *iroij*'s canoe. As the demons reached the canoe, they climbed aboard.

The youngest demon girl chanted

> *Inkat bawit eo rō-totore,*
> *rieb katak oh, jilib, biduk kañi ko bako.*

> The stick floats on the ocean,
> It drops from the canoe and all are eaten by the sharks.

She swept every demon from the canoe. Then she saw her parents and older sister fly to the canoe. The young girl laid down the sticks.

"Come with us now," her parents called to her.

"I wish to stay with my husband," she told them, and called, "Older sister, come back with me."

The parents turned to the *iroij*. "If you take our daughters, keep them with you all the time. If you climb the coconut tree or if you go fishing, they must always be there beside you."

"Agreed," the *iroij* said, and together the demon sisters and the *iroij* sailed back to Rongerik.

One day, much later, the *iroij* went fishing by himself. Black clouds gathered above him as a big wind swooped in. The *iroij* paddled hard against the wind and waves, but to no avail. Right then he remembered his promise. "I didn't take the girls with me."

He was blown away, away, away until he disappeared. Up to this very day no one has seen the *iroij*. The demon sisters returned to Ujae.

*Jidip inoñ jidim jedu.*
That's the end of the story.

# DEMON FART

*Ujae is in* Kaben Meto, *the bottom of the ocean. Everything ends up there. Garbage floating in the ocean, canoes sailing off course, and demons. You can find lots of demons in* Kaben Meto.

**Lade** LAH-reh

*kubañ*
  koo-BAHNG

*baret* BEYE-ret

A man named **Lade** had pet fish, the *kubañ* and the *baret*. As he sat making fire, he would call to his fish so he could feed them.

> *Kubañ lulu to ilik to.*
> *Badet lulu to imijini na.*

> Kubañ come together and come to me.
> Baret, you come to me, too.

**Likirebjel** lee-kih-REB-jel

There lived a demon nearby, the demon woman **Likirebjel**. She heard Lade calling his fish.

> *"Ejoram it ke le?"* the demon woman chanted. "Do you have any fire?"
> *"It eo le,"* Lade chanted back. "Yes, I do."
> *"Ejoram jolak ke?"* continued the demon woman. "Is the fire already going?"
> *"Jolak eo le,"* Lade finished. "The fire is here."

The demon woman called Likirebjel ate both the fire and Lade. She had herself a good cooked meal.

When she finished, she felt so good she farted.

*Kañ it em, kañ Lade.*
*Rub*!

Eat him, I eat Lade.
Phht! She farted Lade right out.

The demon woman called Likirebjel looked back in surprise.

"*Kwalok ie le lade?*" the demon woman called out. "Where did you come from, Lade?"
"*Ilo jiñ eo emot lok,*" answered Lade. "You farted and I came out."

Lade went out to feed his fish.
The demon woman called Likirebjel got really mad. She scooped up half the island, along with some people, canoes, and coconut trees. She ate them all. She was preparing, preparing to eat the man Lade.
Lade sat at home building a fire. The woman demon called Likirebjel called to him again.

"*Ejoram it ke le?*" the demon woman chanted. "Do you have any fire?"
"*It eo le,*" Lade chanted back. "Yes, I do."
"*Ejoram jolak ke?*" continued the demon woman. "Is the fire already going?"
"*Jolak eo le,*" Lade finished. "The fire is here."

Once again she ate Lade and his fire.

*Kañ it em, kañ Lade*
*Rub*!

Eat him, I eat Lade.

Phht! She farted Lade right out.

*Kwalok ie le lade?*
Where did you come from, Lade?
*Ilo jiñ eo emot lok*
You farted and I came out.

Lade laughed and started catching clams at the reef.
The demon woman called *Likirebjel* got even madder. She chomped down another chunk of land.

*You go there today you'll see a river, because she swallowed that part of the island. Kids race toy canoes there now.*

The demon woman called Likirebjel ate the entire island preparing to eat Lade. She wanted to block up her stomach to make sure Lade wouldn't pop out again.
Having caught a basket of clams, Lade built a fire. The demon woman called Likirebjel screamed out at him.

*Ejoram it ke le?*
Do you have any fire?
*It eo le,*
Yes, I do.
*Ejoram jolak ke?*
Is the fire already going?
*Jolak eo le.*
The fire is here.

She swallowed him. She swallowed the fire. She

swallowed his basket of clams. She farted. *Rub!*
Phht!

She farted, all right, but Lade got stuck with the
trees and land and everything. The little man stayed
inside! The demon laughed and danced.

Lade found his basket and grabbed himself a
clam. He sliced at the demon woman's belly. As he
cut, he chanted.

*Ikañ ah ane ejab metak lojeō.*
She eats the island and her stomach doesn't hurt.

Maybe the demon woman called Likirebjel looked like she still danced, but she was in a lot of pain. Lade cut and chanted.

*Ikañ ah ane ejab metak lojeō.*
She eats the canoes and her stomach doesn't hurt.

With each cut, the demon screamed. With each cut, Lade chanted:

*Ikañ ah ane ejab metak lojeō.*
She eats the house and her stomach doesn't hurt.

With each cut, the demon's body grew weaker.

*Ikañ ah ane ejab metak lojeō.*
She eats the trees and her stomach doesn't hurt.

The demon woman grew so weak, she couldn't even fart. Lade finished his chant:

*Ikañ laidikdik abñeñe le eo Lade ejkab metak aj-jeiō.*
When she eats Lade, her stomach really starts to hurt.

The demon flopped over, dead. Lade climbed out and called to his fish. They were ready to eat.

*Jidip inoñ jidim jedu.*

That's the end of the story.

*If you go there you will see one hill. The hill is the demon's body. You might also see a small rock that's shaped like a stick, sitting there on a larger rock. That's Lade's fire-making stick.*

# TOBOLAR, COCONUT BOY

*You know the story of Tobolar, the first coconut? The one you heard is not the one. This is the story. Etto im etto . . . Long and long time past . . .*

**Lewatonmour**
le-WAH-tuhn-moh-oor

**Relik** REE-lihk

**Eniwetak** en-ee-WEH-tahk

**Lewatonmour** lived on Aelōñlaplap with her two sons and her brother, *Iroij* **Relik** of the Ralik Islands. Hardly any food grew on the island. Her two sons complained of hunger all the time. And Lewatonmour needed extra food. So *Iroij* Relik decided to take them all away. The family sailed to a small island called Bikin in **Eniwetak** [Enewetok].

*I've never been there, but they say there is a small island called Bikin.*

Soon after they arrived, Lewatonmour delivered another boy. This third son arrived as a small white sprout. Lewatonmour loved her odd little son nonetheless. She named him Tobolar. Each day she carried her newborn everywhere with her. Each night she nursed little Tobolar and lovingly sang him to sleep.

Lewatonmour's other sons didn't like this odd boy. "Why do you spend all your time with that . . . that . . . thing?" they said to their mother.

"This is my newest son," Lewatonmour told them, "your little brother."

"He's not a brother!" the oldest shouted. "He's not even a boy."

"You never take care of us!" the other complained. "You never cook or anything. Get rid of that thing. Or we will."

Lewatonmour began to fear for her smallest son. So one moonless night Lewatonmour snuck out to the end of the island and buried little Tobolar. It broke her heart, but she had to protect him from the other sons.

The older boys wondered what had happened. Tobolar had disappeared so suddenly. But their mother told them nothing.

Lewatonmour visited Tobolar whenever she

could. After a few days a small sprout grew up in the very spot where Lewatonmour had buried him. Tears fell from her eyes. "Tobolar, my beautiful son."

After several more days, a leaf grew.

"Five little fingers!" she exclaimed.

Her older boys wanted to know what she was up to. "She disappears every day, all day." Early the next morning the boys followed their mother as she snuck off into the bush.

At the end of the island, the boys watched as their mother picked up a brown nut that lay at the foot of a tree. They stared as she broke the nut open and ate from it. And they cried in amazement as their mother sang lovingly to the tree.

From then on the boys visited the Tobolar tree every day. They climbed the tree and ate and drank from the many different kinds of nuts that continued to grow.

Lewatonmour and her family no longer suffered from hunger. Tobolar provided everything for them, from the sap of the tree to the sweet white meat of the coconut.

*That's why we have the many kinds of coconuts and coconut parts today, from that little white sprout of a child, Tobolar.*

*Jidip inoñ jidim jedu.*
That's the end of the story.

# EQ, THE DRAWING OF THE LINES

When the sands first met the sea, **Lowa** created colorful island worlds. He shaped the islands and moved them about the ocean. Coral reefs sparkled under the bright water. Waves softly slip-sloshed the sand, welcomed by the whispery green of coconut trees. Each floating isle became a special place; each dot of land earned its own name.

*eq* [EH-aw] tattoo

**Lowa** LOH-wah

"Finished," said Lowa as he fit the last name to the last dot. Lowa then thought to place living creatures on his beautiful islands, living creatures to celebrate the beauty of the islands and sing songs about the one who made it all.

As colorful as each island was, however, the living creatures all looked dingy dull. Every bird Lowa created looked like one bird, and all fish looked the same. Each shell he made looked as plain as the last, with no color and no design. And Lowa's people couldn't tell one from another and didn't know a stranger from their brother.

Confusion was everywhere. Lowa's creatures wandered from dawn to dusk looking for someone, anyone familiar. Whole days slipped by. People might walk right by a friend and never know it. Animals couldn't find their own mothers, and the fish, the poor fish, swam 'round and 'round and 'round. Was that a reflection, or another fish swimming by? Time came and went with never any thought for the creator who brought life to the island creatures.

Lowa looked down from his sky world and saw that his creations had no time for him. He saw them forget who had made their tiny islands. He watched as each creature grew confused, lost, and completely unhappy. Lowa became as unhappy as the loneliest fish in the sea.

"How can I bring my world into order?" he asked. "How can I make my creations happy? How can I make sure every creature will remember me?"

In answer to his question, a chant floated by like a cloud.

> *Paint the fish,*
> *Color the birds,*
> *Create special drawings on the lizard, the rat.*

"Those two," said Lowa, and smiled. Those two lived in the sky world with Lowa. Those two were the artists **Lewoj** and **Lanij**.

**Lewoj** LEH-wohj
**Lanij** LAH-neej

Lowa immediately called on those two and told them, "Bring your art to my islands. Color the animals. Draw on the fish and birds. Design no two alike! Each must look different from the others so that everyone and everything will know themselves from their brother."

> *Design well the lines.*

Lewoj and Lanij stepped off the sky world. They jumped down to begin their work. The artists of the sky landed right on their feet on the beautiful island of Aelōñlaplap.

"Those two," chuckled Lowa.

You can still see the holes where they landed. The place is called **Jimunne**.

Jimunne
[jih-MUHN-nay]
heel

Lewoj and Lanij stepped out of the holes and brushed themselves off. Those two artists immediately began designing Lowa's island creatures.

*Paint the fish*
*Color the birds*
*Create special drawings on the lizard, the rat.*
*Design well the lines.*

As Lewoj and Lanij chanted, they covered the skin of fish with zigzags and sharp lines. The artists of the sky colored birds with bright feathers and beaks.

*Zigzags that flash*
*'Round deep, dark dots.*
*A miracle, the color falls from heaven.*
*Design well the lines.*

Animals flew in from all the newly named islands to be designed by those two. Lewoj and Lanij kept busy, chanting and making special marks, lines, and colors on lizards and rats' tails, on octopus legs and wings of flies. Every animal, each creature of the land, even every shell and little creature of the sea got its own color and style.

Greens, reds, and browns exploded across the sky. The sea shimmered with silver grays, and a rainbow of colors swirled and swam through the reefs. Lowa's new world celebrated the artists of the sky in each unique bird and every brilliantly colored fish.

"Now bring your art to the people," Lowa called down from up above.

Lewoj and Lanij approached the people of the island worlds. "You have to draw the lines so you become beautiful," Lewoj told them. "The fish in the water are striped and have lines."

"So, too, human beings should have stripes and lines," continued Lanij. "The eǫ we bring for everyone."

Lewoj finished by telling the people, "Everything disappears after death. But the eǫ, the designs, are you. They'll be with you when you leave your island home."

> Beat the drums,
> Clap your hands!
> Joy fills these artists of the sky.
> Design well the lines.

Drums rumbled. People chanted. Lewoj and Lanij created designs that danced over the skin of Lowa's people. The eǫ of the skin showed off the beauty of the islands. The blackness matched the darkness of the sea swallow. Lines copied exactly the sharpness of the angelfish stripes. Lewoj and Lanij drew shapes like the turtle's back and dots like the shells of the sea. Designs echoed sharks' teeth and crabs' legs, canoes and wind-filled sails, waves of the sea, and clouds towering above.

The artists of the sky helped each man and every woman know one from the other. So, too, their drawings showed rank, whether king or commoner, prince or leader of a clan. The people knew an *iroij*, a chief, from the special drawings on his head and neck.

The people of the islands sang in celebration of the eǫ and the gods who brought it.

*Our song floats on clouds of joy,*
*Floating to the artists of the sky.*
*Beat the drums, clap your hands!*
*The ink-black birds*
*Swoop about the sky,*
*Shadows of the eǫ's darkness;*
*Design well the lines, artists of the skin!*

*Silence settles over the drums,*
*So the artists won't blacken their hands.*
*They should not hear, not hear the drum-*
*ming,*
*As they draw the lines, the dots, designs.*
*Design well the lines, artists of the skin!*

Lewoj and Lanij, the gods of the *eǫ*, brought the tattoo to the island world. They showed Lowa's creatures the beauty of their islands. These two taught the *iroij* and his people how to drum and draw and chant. The artists of the sky helped keep alive the memory of the one who created the island worlds.

*Lines grow to sharp designs.*
*Finished are the dots!*
*A miracle, the color falls from heaven.*
*Design well the lines, artists of the skin!*

*Jidip inoñ jidim jedu.*
That's the end of the story.

# JIRABELBEL AND RIWITIÑTIÑ

**Jirabelbel**
  jih-RAH-bel-bel

**Riwitiñtiñ**
  ree-WIH-ting-
  ting

The islanders loved to surf, to ride the waves all the way to shore. On Lae, the *iroij*, Riwitiñtiñ, declared a contest to see who could surf the fastest. He placed a banana on the beach. Whoever made it to the banana first won.

The *iroij*'s wife played the drums. She played the drums while she sang of what a great surfer her husband was.

While Riwitiñtiñ surfed, an *iroij* named Jirabelbel stole Riwitiñtiñ's beautiful wife. He just grabbed her, dropped her in his canoe, and took her to his home on Ujae.

Riwitiñtiñ sailed to Ujae that night and stole his wife back.

Jirabelbel immediately sailed to Lae. He met Riwitiñtiñ and they fought. They fought hard. They fought until Jirabelbel killed Riwitiñtiñ. Jirabelbel took Riwitiñtiñ's wife back to Ujae.

However, Riwitiñtiñ didn't die. So he sailed to Ujae again. He waited until it was dark and went to a place called **Toelae**, near the reef.

**Toelae** TOH-leye

Riwitiñtiñ told his men to wait. He took his club and made his way to Jirabelbel's house. While Jirabelbel slept, his mother went out to relieve herself. She saw Riwitiñtiñ hiding. She started chanting:

*Ikiki itenak ie boñ ij lo am*
*Riwitiñtiñ to tak*

*im bukbuke Jirabelbel im mottan wot*
*jijdikdik.*

I sleep and in my dreams at night
I see Riwitiñtiñ come from his canoe and
Cut Jirabelbel like a chicken.

Jirabelbel shouted, "What are you trying to say? I
killed him already!"
Riwitiñtiñ snuck up to Jirabelbel's window.
The mother chanted again:

*Ikiki itenak ie boñ ij lo am*
*Riwitiñtiñ to tak*
*im bukbuke Jirabelbel im mottan wot*
*jijdikdik.*

I sleep and in my dreams at night
I see Riwitiñtiñ come from his canoe and
Cut Jirabelbel like a chicken.

Jirabelbel stuck his head out the window and
shouted at her, "We're trying to sleep, old woman,
and you keep talking!"
Riwitiñtiñ took his stick and killed Jirabelbel,
cutting him into pieces. Riwitiñtiñ grabbed his wife
and ran off. The old lady cried, but there was nothing she could do. The old lady buried her son.
Riwitiñtiñ sailed home to Lae.

*Riwitiñtiñ and his men are the small sharks you*
*see swimming there. Jirabelbel turned into a* **kōno**     **kōno** KEUH-noh
*tree.*

*Jidip inoñ jidim jedu.*
That's the end of the story.

# LŌ BEIBAT, THE FOOLISH LITTLE SQUID

**Lō Beibat**
leuh BAY-bat

**Lijuwawa** lee-joo-
WAH-wah

*On the island of Ujae there were two women. One was **Lijuwawa**, and the other, who knows anymore?*

Once, as these two women walked the reef, Lijuwawa said, "Hey, this is good."

"Oh, yeah, yeah, look," the other woman agreed, "the tide is really low."

As they talked, a *kweat* crawled out of a hollow in the coral. "Talk, talk, talk, you two! And I'm right here. How come you don't take me and cook me and eat me?"

The women carried the *kweat* to shore. Together they dug an *um*, an underground oven. When they finished, the women stared at the squid in confusion.

"What's taking so long, you two?" the *kweat* asked.

"We're not really sure how to cook you," they said.

*tilan* [tee-LAHN] pumice, porous volcanic rock

*marjej* [MAHR-jehj] a weed called the "toilet paper plant"; it has almost no woody parts.

"*Dekem dekem ta?*" Lijuwawa asked. "Which rock do I use?"

"*Tilan*," the *kweat* answered with a sly squid smile.

"*Kanem kanem ta?*" Lijuwawa then asked. "What wood do I use?"

"*Marjej*," the *kweat* said, holding back a laugh.

"*Bilkem bilkem ta?*" Lijuwawa asked the squid. "What leaf do I use?"

"**Atat**," the *kweat* told them, nearly bursting with laughter.

The women gathered the *tilan* rocks and *marjej* wood and lit the oven. They then placed the *kweat* inside and covered him with the *atat* leaves. The two went off to prepare some food to eat with the *kweat*. Deep inside the *um*, the sly squid finally let his laughter fly.

*It's important to tell you the* kweat *was lying. These are no good for cooking. You see,* marjej *hardly burns,* tilan *won't heat, and* atat *are too small to cover the* um. *That's why the* kweat *was laughing. He'd tricked them.*

The women chanted as they collected coconut.

> *Bijbij ie debin ni*
> *marōmrōm waini*
> *ñōre, ñōre elōn ijen.*

> Kicking the coconut tree,
> The coconut falls.
> Gnaw, gnaw that coconut, we sure got a lot.

"Okay," Lijuwawa finally said. "We got enough to eat with the *kweat*."

Now, because of his little trick, the *kweat* didn't cook at all. Instead, he snuck out of the *um* after leaving a disgusting little surprise for the women.

The women pulled aside the leaves, scooped out what they thought was cooked squid, and began to eat.

*atat* [aht-AHT] a ground-covering plant, traditionally used to make a fine fiber; its leaves are very small.

"Oh, oh, yuck," said Lijuwawa in disgust, spitting out the *kweat*'s "surprise."

The other woman spit, too. "This isn't cooked *kweat*, this is *kweat* poop."

Lijuwawa said, "Don't you worry. Don't you worry about that. Tomorrow we'll visit that tricky little squid. For now, let's sleep." And they did, still hungry.

The next morning the women went out onto the reef again. They talked about the low tide and waited. Soon the *kweat* stuck his head from his hiding place. "Talk, talk, talk, you two! And I'm right here. How come you don't take me and cook me and eat me."

The women carried the *kweat* to shore.

"But we don't know how to cook you," Lijuwawa said. "*Dekem dekem ta?* What rock do I use?"

"*Tilan*," the *kweat* answered, with another sly smile.

Lijuwawa turned to the other woman and whispered, "That rock's too crumbly. Let's use **dekalal**; that should fire up very hot."

Lijuwawa turned back to the *kweat*. "*Kanem kanem ta?* What wood do I use?"

"*Marjej*," the *kweat* said, holding his laugh.

"No, no, no," Lijuwawa whispered to her friend. "We'll use **koñe**. I bet it'll burn scorching hot."

To the squid, she said, "*Bilkem bilkem ta?* What leaf do I use?"

"*Atat*," the *kweat* told them, nearly bursting again.

"Again he's lying!" whispered Lijuwawa. "**Bilkin mā** is the leaf we'll try. It's so big, the heat will be sure to stay trapped inside."

The women gathered the wood and rocks and lit the oven. It burned hot, very hot. They threw the

**dekalal**
[reh-KAY-lahl] basaltic rock; it holds heat well, through as many as fifty firings in an earth oven.

**koñe** [KOHNG-eh] wood of the ironwood tree

**bilkin mā**
BIHL-kihn meh

*kweat* inside and quickly covered it with the *bilkin mā*. The *kweat* screamed.

The women just laughed, busying themselves with collecting coconuts.

"Dig me out!" the *kweat* cried. "I'm cooking!"

The two chanted to drown out the screams.

> *Bijbij ie debin ni*
> *marōmrōm waini*
> *ñōre, ñōre elōn ijen.*

> Kicking the coconut tree,
> The coconut falls.
> Gnaw, gnaw that coconut, we sure got a lot.

Soon the screams stopped. The women opened the oven. The *kweat* looked all delicious, so nicely baked. But they checked just to make sure.

Lijuwawa and her friend sat under a *kiden* tree. They ate, ate, ate, and ate the *kweat*. Then they nodded off to sleep. Soon, Lijuwawa heard a sound coming from the ocean.

> *Iwa tak le*
> *iwa tak jen*
> *kabin lon ijo*
> *Romini ko ie raititi ko ie*
> *umin kiden en lik kiden ta kiden ta kiden.*

> Cooking under the coconut tree,
> Under the *kiden* tree, the *kiden,* the *kiden,*
> the *kiden.*

Lijuwawa shook her sleepy friend, "There's something singing. It's far away, but it sounds big, like a demon!"

"What?" the woman asked, "I don't hear anything."

The sound came again, much closer.

> *Iwa tak le*
> *iwa tak jen*
> *kabin lon ijo*
> *Romini ko ie raititi ko ie*
> *umin kiden en lik kiden ta kiden ta kiden.*

> Cooking under the coconut tree,
> Under the *kiden* tree, the *kiden,* the *kiden,*
> the *kiden.*

The two women screamed. They grabbed some
pandanus leaves and conjured up some magic.

"Do we go hide up the coconut tree?" they asked
the leaves.

"No," read the magic.

The demon voice sang again, closer.

"Dig a hole to hide?"

"No," the magic read.

Louder and louder the singing grew.

"Swim away? Hide on top of the house? In the
bushes?"

"No, no, no."

"Then where?!"

They called on the magic one last time. It read,
"Hide in the ceiling of your house."

The two ran as a huge tentacle flopped onto the
shore. It was the *kweat*'s mother, a demon-sized
squid. The tentacle began searching, searching,
searching over the entire island.

In the ceiling, the women consulted the leaves
again.

"Should we kill the demon *kweat* with a stick?"

Lijuwawa asked frantically.

"No."

"How about a coconut leaf?" the other woman asked.

Again the answer was no.

"The thorn of the pandanus leaf?" Lijuwawa shouted. The tentacle turned toward the house.

"Yes!" the magic read.

The women ripped a line of thorns from the edge of the pandanus leaf.

The tentacle reached into the house. The women held back their screams. The tentacle climbed a ridgepole slowly, crawling into the ceiling.

"*Jotok joko eo, jeke bin jeke bin jolak!*" Lijuwawa chanted. "Cut off the arm!"

She sliced with the thorns. The tentacle fell lifeless to the floor.

The demon *kweat* screeched, but another tentacle shot out of the water, heading straight for the house.

"*Jotok joko eo, jeke bin jeke bin jolak!* Cut off the arm!"

Lijuwawa sliced again, and another tentacle fell lifeless to the ground. Another tentacle reached out of the ocean. Lijuwawa kept slicing, and tentacles kept falling and shooting out of the ocean until a whole pile of demon tentacles lay lifeless on the floor.

The island fell quiet. The women crawled out from the ceiling. They built another *um*. Together the two women dragged the demon squid into the oven and had a grand feast.

*Jidip inoñ jidim jedu.*
That's the end of the story.

# LŌ KOKELŌK

**Lō Kokelōk** leuh
koh-KAY-leuhk

*I'm telling you a story of an* iroij *named Lō Kokelōk.*

*Iroij* Lō Kokelōk lived on Ebon with his wife. So many people lived on the island there was hardly any grass on the ground. When Lō Kokelōk's wife became pregnant, all the people gathered to congratulate them. *Iroij* Lō Kokelōk announced his intent to go traveling island to island looking for wondrous gifts for his pregnant wife, the tradition called **bōkanje**.

**bōkanje** [beuh-KAHN-jeh]
the tradition of
traveling island
to island look-
ing for gifts for
a pregnant wife

Each day he was gone, Lō Kokelōk's wife sat oceanside to wait for her husband. Each day, in the midst of the waiting, she chanted:

> *Lō Kokelōk ie, Lō Kokelōk oooo.*
> *Item jañinbel jañinbar ke kinerro,*
> *ikililok, oh ijerleak lok, oh,*
> *wan kabo wan kabo,*
> *ebo lik ebo lik, ekobakbak kajkwe.*
>
> Lō Kokelōk, where is Lō Kokelōk, oooo.
> I've been waiting so long,
> I sleep, oh, you're not there, oh,
> Sail away, sail away,
> Set your sail for the ocean side.

Each day, as her chant settled over the water, Lō

Kokelōk stopped at an island. He stopped at Namdrik looking for mats, at Maloelap to pick breadfruit. He sailed far north to the islands in Kaben Meto to find flowers only an *iroij* could wear. On one small island he found a **kōlkōl**, an animal capable of imitating any noise: the wind, people, chickens, or canoes.

*kōlkōl*
[KEUHL-keuhl]
an animal capable of imitating any noise

Each day the *iroij*'s wife returned home without him.

Loneliness became the pregnant woman's only companion. Weeks and months sailed by, separating her more and more from her husband and her happiness.

When Lō Kokelōk finally returned to Ebon, he met only an empty, silent shore.

"No one's here," Lō Kokelōk marveled aloud to his crew. The people of Ebon had always met his boat.

As he stepped onto the shore, he told his men to wait in the **wallap**. Shadowed figures moved quickly beyond the trees from ocean to lagoon, from lagoon to ocean. It looked as if there were a lot of people running back and forth, back and forth.

*wallap*
[WAHL-lahp]
a canoe

"Why would they be running?" thought the *iroij*. "Unless they're trying to hide."

He put the *kōlkōl* on his shoulder and walked onto the island. It was very still. No people running. Nothing. The island appeared darker than Lō Kokelōk remembered.

His wife appeared right near where he had seen the shadows running. "*Iakwe,*" she said, quietly.

"*Iakwe,*" he answered. "Where is everyone?"

"Oh," his wife said, "the people went oceanside to fish."

"And you're here by yourself?" he asked.

"Yes. I've been waiting for you." She moved

deeper into the darkness between the trees. "Now we should join them. Come."

Lō Kokelōk's wife no longer looked pregnant. Where was the child?

"You go first," he said.

"No, you. I can't go before the *iroij*," she said.

Through the odd darkness of the day they walked, Lō Kokelōk leading carefully through the brush. His wife moved with great speed and silence. A moment before she nearly ran him down, the animal brushed Lō Kokelōk's shoulder. He turned. His wife's face hung just inches from his own.

"If you are in a hurry, you can lead the way," Lō Kokelōk said to her.

"People will want to greet you after so long a time gone," she said. "Keep going."

They started down the path again, his wife moving up quickly and quietly behind him. The *kōlkōl* rubbed his shoulder again. He turned to see a bit of saliva hanging from his wife's mouth. Lō Kokelōk knew the truth now and wished he hadn't stayed away so long. The old legends said a lonely pregnant woman always turned into a *mejenkwaad,* a demon. It must have happened to his wife.

As they neared oceanside, Lō Kokelōk asked, "How come I can't hear anyone?"

"They left already," she answered gruffly. "They're getting ready to meet you. Stop talking and let's go back."

Lō Kokelōk hesitated. "Wait. I have to pee."

"Be quick."

Lō Kokelōk stepped behind a *kañol* tree. He put the *kōlkōl* on the ground and told it, "Make the sound of me."

"Shshshshshsh," muttered the *kōlkōl.*

Lō Kokelōk ran to the village. It lay silent and

empty. "She's eaten them all," he cried. "What did she do to our child?"

He picked up several **kor**. He tied one to a tree at one side of the island. He ran to the other side to do the same.

"Shshshshshsh," muttered the *kōlkōl*, as the demon-wife waited.

He snapped off one **jubbub in mañ** and ran on to the end of the island, where his crew waited in the canoe.

"Shshshshshsh," the *kōlkōl* muttered.

The demon-wife grew impatient with waiting. "Are you still back there?"

"Shshshshshsh," the *kōlkōl* muttered on and on.

She looked behind the tree. She growled when she saw the animal, ate it, and ran off, calling

> *Lō Kokelōk ie, Lō Kokelōk oooo,*
> Lō Kokelōk, where is Lō Kokelōk, oooo.

The *kor* answered her call, *ooooooo*. She ran to it. Angered by this second trick, she ate the *kor* in a single crunch.

Lō Kokelōk sailed off, leaving his demon-wife on her lonely island crying

> *Lō Kokelōk ie, Lō Kokelōk oooo,*
> Lō Kokelōk, where is Lō Kokelōk, oooo.

Another *kor* answered her call, *ooooooo*. She leapt at it, tore it apart, and screamed her husband's name until it echoed off the ocean's waves.

She stretched her neck up through the coconut trees, up to the clouds, looking, looking, looking across the Ratak chain, then the Ralik chain. She

**kor** [kohr]
coconut shells with a hole in the middle

**jubbub in mañ**
[JOOB-boob ihn mahng]
pandanus thorn

couldn't see him anywhere. She looked south, then north and saw the *wallap* heading to Namdrik.

All the men cried out in fear when they saw the demon-woman's head floating just below the clouds. Lō Kokelōk chanted:

> *Kurlōn kurlōn, kwarlōñ kwarlōñ,*
> *Wiake to waj, ohhhhhhhh.*

> Fly, fly, high, high,
> Fly off to the sky, ohhhhhhh.

He threw the *jubbub in mañ* as hard as he could into the air. The floating head chased, chased, chased it up into the sky. When her head sailed down again, screaming after the thorn, she was far from the island of Ebon. She and her body got so very lost and confused, she disappeared for good.

> *Jidip inoñ jidim jedu.*
> That's the end of the story.

## JORJU ARRE

I hadn't planned on meeting with Jorju, but my "official" storyteller (Nitwa Jeik) had to leave two days after I arrived, so the Ujae mayor introduced me to Jorju. He was sitting outside his house making *ekkwal* when we first met. As I took a picture he said, "Oh, thank you very much."

A polite and funny man, Jorju was ready the first day we recorded his stories. Dressed up in a bright green flowered shirt and a faded blue cap with a *lei* of flowers on it, he beckoned me to sit on a mat laid out just for me. He told the others gathered there, "Quiet now. Time for work."

Jorju introduced himself very officially into the tape recorder. He gave his full name and said he was

**Jorju Arre**
JOHR-joo AHR-reh

***ekkwal***
[EK-kwahl]
sennit, or
coconut rope

from "Ujae Atoll, Marshall Islands, Trust Territory of the United States." As would happen often, a big laugh burst out of him.

Born in the very house we shared stories in, he had "many brothers and sisters." His mother died when he was five. As a young boy he climbed coconut, pandanus, and breadfruit trees to collect food, carried wood for cooking, fished, and hunted for octopus.

His grandparents raised him and taught him many important aspects of his culture, including ***jitdam kapeel*** and ***mōnmōnbwij.*** If some of the sons or daughters visit, feed them. If you don't, they will go back and tell the *iroij*. The *iroij* will kick you off the land or not help take care of you.

Jorju worked as a health assistant in Rongelap, Majuro, and Ujae. During World War II, he worked with the Japanese, cooking for important people. He decorated the table for them in Kwajalein and Rongelap. After the war he started a family. "I was really handsome and the women were chasing me."

Jorju always had stories ready to share, always wore a dress shirt, and always made sure tea was ready. Little children liked to sit around and listen while he told stories, since often they had never heard them. Jorju made sure they sat and were quiet, an amazing accomplishment with the children on these tiny islands.

He was animated during his tellings, drawing out stories on his bed and pulling a piece of paper out of a small hole in the floor to punctuate a surprise. He liked to throw English phrases in to make me laugh. One evening, as I entered his house, Jorju said, "Come sit near me if you love me."

He learned his stories from a couple of old men from Ujae. "If anyone asked," he told me, "those two would tell stories. I asked." He has told the stories only to his grandson because "he asked." No one asks Jorju anymore because they don't know he knows stories. "Now people only think of money," he says. "People have lost the *iakwe*."

"I'm running out of words, but the thing I will say is that people must love each other."

Jorju died a year later.

JORJU ARRE

# THE LOST BOY

*Bwebwenato in Aelōñlaplap. A story from Aelōñlaplap.*

**Lejla** LEJ-lah

**Letujāwa** leh-
TOO-jeh-wah

**Jeh** jeh

Two pregnant women, **Lejla** and **Letujāwa**, lived on the island of **Jeh**. By tradition they bathed often in the ocean, where they first met each other.

Lejla asked, "How many months are you?"

"Four months," Letujāwa said. "And you?"

"Same like you."

Over time the two became good friends.

Lejla asked, "How are you feeling, my friend?"

"Heavy," Letujāwa said. "And you?"

"Same like you."

Near the end of their pregnancies, the two couldn't be separated.

Lejla asked, "How are you today?"

"Ready to give birth," Letujāwa said. "And you?"

"Same like you."

So the two made a plan.

"If you have a boy and I have a girl," Lejla said, "we'll make them husband and wife."

"But if they are both boys," Letujāwa said, "they'll be sure to fight."

**Eb** eb

**Woja** WOH-jah

As the women laughed together and prepared to give birth, two *iroij*, one from the northern island of **Eb**, the other from the southern island of **Woja**, stumbled upon the women. The *iroij* took the two as

170

their wives, separating the pregnant friends.

The women gave birth. At Eb, Letujāwa gave birth to a girl. At Woja, Lejla gave birth to a boy. The two friends could not fulfill their promise.

Soon after giving birth, Lejla went with some of the Woja women to bathe and oil herself in the ocean. She brought her son along in a basket. As the women oiled their hair, the wind pushed the basket onto the ocean. Lejla screamed. The women ran into the water but they could only watch as the basket disappeared behind the waves.

Farther north, on Eb, rain sprinkled from a scatter of clouds. Eb people say when it sprinkles rain there is something at Jiadel, a special place near the lagoon. The *iroij* told some boys to go and see what was there. "If it's **bijbeto**," he said, "throw it away. If it's coconuts, bring them here to eat."

**bijbeto**
[BIZH-be-doh]
flotsam (floating wreckage)

The boys saw a basket sitting on some rocks. "It's moving," said one. They ran quickly back to the *iroij* and told him what they'd seen.

"Why didn't you bring it with you?" he asked.

"You didn't tell us what to do if it was crying."

"Crying?" asked Lejla.

"Like my brother," said the one boy.

"Like MY brother," said the other and hit his brother.

"Let me go there," Lejla begged her husband, so they went.

The *iroij* fished out the basket. "It's a baby boy," he told his wife.

"Let me bring him up with our daughter," Lejla asked her husband.

The *iroij* gave her the baby boy, but didn't like the idea.

As that boy, **Kikā**, grew up, the *iroij* learned to hate him.

"He just plays, plays, and plays," the *iroij* told his wife. "Not like our little girl."

"He's our child, too."

"He's nothing. He just washed up on the shore like *bijbeto*."

The *iroij* refused to let Kikā eat with his family. He'd send the boy off with just scraps of food.

"He can have my food," the *iroij*'s daughter offered.

"No. He's nothing but flotsam, so he gets nothing but flotsam."

But the *iroij*'s daughter would sneak food out to her brother.

Once, the *iroij* saw Kikā with the food. "You stole that food."

"I didn't steal it," he answered. "Your daughter gave it . . . "

"You lie!" the *iroij* yelled at him. "You're nothing but trouble. You don't belong here, you don't belong to me, you're nothing but *bijbeto*!"

Kikā ran off. "I'm going to look for my real mother and father."

Near the lagoon side of Eb, his sister caught up with him. "Kikā, you can't leave me alone."

"You stay. Eat all the good food they give you."

"No," she said. "I'm coming with you."

"You have to stay here!"

"Everywhere you go," she swore to him, "I go. The place you die, I'll die. All your relatives will be mine, your mother and father, mine. Don't stop me. I'm part of you."

"Then you must bring with you a waterless coconut," the boy told his sister, "and gather up a little sand."

She did as her brother said. Together they made their way to the end of Eb. Kikā jumped into the channel, singing:

> *Itok joro aō ilo to in.*
> *Joklae im belik iñjuōn eo la, iñruo la*
> *iñ im bar iñ*
> *im kebelok le, limin añod eo.*

> Come let's swim to the other island.
> We'll pass the first channel, the second channel
> And the other channels
> And we'll reach the next island.

His body lifted off the sand and flew over the channel. Landing on the next island, he signaled for his sister to follow. She shouted, "I don't know how to swim!"

The boy chanted for her,

> *Kij mān ne im jer bokan en ne.*
> Eat a little coconut and spill a little sand.

She spilled the sand across the channel. The water parted. She ran over the dry channel, joining her brother. The water refilled the channel as she stepped onto the sand.

They ran to the next channel. The boy chanted, flew over the water, and called for his sister to follow.

> *Kij mān ne im jer bokan en ne.*
> Eat a little coconut and spill a little sand.

She spilled the sand, the water parted, and the

two ran to the next channel. On and on they flew and ran until they arrived at Woja Island.

On the shore of Woja, some little boys were playing **kajer,** flicking a small branch to see who could throw the farthest.

*kajer* [kah-JEHR]
a game

Kikā asked one of them, "Can I borrow your toy?"

"You just walk over here and want to take my *kajer?*" the boy answered. "Make your own."

Kikā asked each boy. Not one gave him the toy, until he asked the littlest boy there.

"How far can you throw it?" asked the littlest boy as he gave Kikā the toy.

Kikā took it, balanced it on a rock, and chanted a bit of magic:

> *Kurlōn kurlōn, kwarlōñ kwarlōñ*
> *Letao bolak wa ne warro,*
> *ñan ikkin mõn im nojnoj lok.*

> Fly fly, high high
> Letao, man of tricks,
> Carry this toy oceanside and hide it well.

Kikā stepped on the branch, sending it twirling into the air. He whacked it hard with a large stick. The little toy flew away and away and away out of sight.

**Likukure** lee-
KOO-koo-reh

**Lōrōkewa** leuh-
reuh-KAY-wah

In a village called **Likukure**, on the other side of Woja, lived *Iroij* **Lōrōkewa**. As the toy sailed across the island, the *iroij* slept. As the toy fell from the sky, Letujāwa, the *iroij*'s wife, stepped out of the house. The little toy struck Letujāwa in her left eye.

"Ah!" she cried. "Lōrōkewa! My husband! Come quick, come quick!"

The *iroij* leapt off his mat, running. "Letujāwa!" He pulled the toy from her eye.

"I want to know who did this," he cried, calling everyone to Likukure.

All the people of Woja gathered. The *iroij* made each place their index finger in his wife's eye socket. "If your finger fits, you threw the stick."

Everyone passed the test.

"Is there anyone left?" *Iroij* Lōrōkewa asked.

"No more."

"None?"

"Not a one."

*Iroij* Lōrōkewa picked up a leaf and ripped it. He held up a small piece, reading its magic. "There are still two who haven't taken the test."

The little boys who had been playing said, "Oh, there're two over there."

Kikā and his sister were brought to him. The *iroij* placed the girl's finger in his wife's eye. It was difficult, but she pulled it back out. Kikā's finger, however, got stuck.

"These are the ones!" the *iroij* cried. "You two shall prepare your own death."

Kikā was forced to sit and roll *ekkwal*, sennit, on his thighs. His sister wove **jaki** for them to be buried in.

*jaki* [JAH-kee]
mats

The people prepared a feast before the execution, as was their tradition. They cooked, scraped breadfruit, gathered fish and coconut.

The *iroij* took a **mejenwōd** and began to sharpen it.

As the sounds of the work and cooking intermingled, a small bird alighted near Kikā and his sister. It sang,

*mejenwōd*
[MEH-jen-weuhr]
a large clamshell

> *Oh Kikā, Kikā, ao?*
> Oh, Kikā, Kikā, what is your mother called?

Kikā answered, "Letujāwa."

The bird continued, "What is your father called?"

Kikā answered, "Lōrōkewa."

The bird concluded,

> *Iakwe, iakwe, iakwe mejān iakwe.*
> We feel sorry for the wife's eye.

One lazy woman, watching over the two, heard the singing and answering. She whispered to some other women. "Listen. Listen to that bird."

"Ah, just go scratch your back over there," one of the women answered.

"No, no," the lazy one insisted. "Listen."

The bird sang again,

> *Oh Kikā, Kikā, ao?*
> Oh, Kikā, Kikā, what is your mother called?

Kikā answered, "Letujāwa."

The bird continued, "What is your father called?"

Kikā answered, "Lōrōkewa."

The bird concluded,

> *Iakwe, iakwe, iakwe mejān iakwe.*
> We feel sorry for the wife's eye.

All the other women stopped cooking and listened. One of them hurried to the *iroij*. The *iroij* stopped sharpening the *mejenwōd*.

The songs filled the air once more. *Iroij* Lōrōkewa asked the boy, "Who are your parents?"

"Letujāwa and Lōrōkewa," the boy said. Letujāwa and Lōrōkewa hugged Kikā and cried. "You're our son come back to us," they told him. "You're our son come back to stay."

JORJU ARRE

# THE TRICKY GIRLS

*Bwebwenato in Lae. A story of Lae Island.*

**Luōj** luh-EUHJ

On the small island **Luōj** lived two really incredibly beautiful girls. You don't see girls like these two today. Their beauty flashed like the sun.

One day, as these two walked along lagoonside, they saw strange men working on a canoe. The strangers had sailed from nearby Lae to fish, but their canoe broke. The *iroij*, a young man, was angry. He worked his men hard to rebuild the canoe. The girls called from the bushes.

"What are those sticks for?" they asked.

The men stopped. They wondered who was there.

"For the canoe," one man answered.

"Whose canoe?" the girls asked.

The men kept looking, but they saw no one.

"The *iroij*," another man said.

"Where is he?" asked the girls.

"Lagoonside," said the *iroij*.

The bushes parted. The two girls stepped out.

"Catch them!" the *iroij* cried out, thinking they were really beautiful, "I want them as my wives."

The men ran, but all the beauty blinded them. The girls moved slowly, keeping the men close. As they ran, the girls chanted:

*Nem juon, nem ruo, jiliblib birukruk.*
*Nem juon, new ruo, jiliblib birukruk.*
*Ketak iam babu lo to en aj po im motlok.*

178

One step, two step, jump into the water and splash.
One step, two step, jump into the water and splash.
Fly into the water and disappear.

The girls jumped into a hole and disappeared. The men searched frantically, but found nothing.

"You couldn't catch those two?" shouted the *iroij*, when the men returned.

"They're really fast for women," the men answered.

"Tomorrow, you get them," ordered the *iroij*. They set up a camp for the night.

The girls climbed out of the hole, laughing. They skipped on home, but never told their parents about the men.

The next morning the girls showered, oiled themselves, and wrapped themselves with stunning flower leis. The girls, flashing an even greater beauty, skipped off toward the lagoon.

The *iroij* soon smelled something beautiful nearby. "*Bwin melu*! What a beautiful smell!" He woke his men.

"What are those sticks for?" the girls started again.

"For the canoe," the men answered, trying to see them.

"Whose canoe?"

"The *iroij*," the men said, noses in the air.

"Where is it?"

"Lagoonside," the *iroij* answered, then shouted, "Find them!"

The men searched the bushes, finding nothing. One heard laughter. Another followed the beautiful smell. They all looked. Over by the canoe stood the two girls.

The *iroij* shouted. The men leapt. The girls ran into the bushes. The men ran as fast as they ever had. The girls always stayed a step ahead, leading the men on a wild chase around the island. As the girls ran, they chanted:

> *Nem juon, nem ruo, jiliblib birukruk.*
> *Nem juon, new ruo, jiliblib birukruk.*
> *Ketak iam babu lo to en aj po im motlok.*

> One step, two step, jump into the water and splash.
> One step, two step, jump into the water and splash.
> Fly into the water and disappear.

One of the men, a long-legged man, caught a girl on the shoulder. She slipped away easily because of the sweet-smelling oil. The girls disappeared into the hole. Not a trace of them remained. The men crowded in to smell the long-legged man's hands.

The *iroij* boiled with anger. "You still didn't catch them?!"

"Those two are very slippery," the long-legged man answered. "I had one, but she slipped away. Come. Smell my hands. It's wonderful!"

"Enough of that!" the *iroij* cried, slapping the man's hands. "You get me those girls!"

"But but but," the men stammered, "they're too fast."

"But they always leap into the same well," the long-legged man said.

Right then they thought of a plan.

As the men talked, the girls jumped out of the hole and skipped home, laughing at their wonderful trick.

Night fell. The men made a net and placed it over the well. They returned to their camp for the night.

The next morning the girls made themselves up to be the sweetest-smelling, most ravishing girls the sun had ever seen. The two giggled silently when they saw the men working on the canoe. They called again, "What are those sticks for?"

Not one man answered. They just worked. The girls moved a little closer. "What are those sticks for?"

Again no one answered. The girls stepped even closer. "What are those sticks for?"

Still no answer. Several times the girls called, and each time they got no answer. Soon they were just steps from the canoe.

The men sprinted at the girls. The girls screamed, running straight for the hole. They jumped and landed in the net. The men gathered them up and carried them to the *iroij*. "We caught them!"

"Into the canoe with them!" the *iroij* cried.

The men wrapped the girls in a mat and placed them in the canoe. They paddled out. When they were far out to sea, the *iroij* said, "Open the mat. I want to see my new wives."

The men unwrapped the girls. A foul smell hit them. Ants and flies crawled out of the girls' eyes.

"They're dead!" the long-legged man cried.

"Throw them away. Throw them away!" The *iroij* cried. The men dumped the bodies into the ocean, but as they hit the water the girls jumped up, the sun flashing off them. "Ah ha, ah ha!" they laughed. "You foolish men!" The men tried to grab them, but were blinded by a beautiful light.

JORJU ARRE

# THE FOOLISH *IROIJ*

*Morning, morning. You came again to listen to this old man. I have another story, but you have to listen to how this story is different. You have to listen to the other side of the story. Bwebwenato in Rongerik. A story of Rongerik.*

Over on Rongerik lived an *iroij* and his wife, the *lejale*. The *iroij* really spoiled his wife. Everything she wanted he gave her. Day or night, he would fetch any kind of fish or coconut. He thought he could keep her happy. He thought he could keep her.

Every day was the same. "I need fish," the *lejale* would tell her husband. Immediately he would get fish. But almost as fast she would say, "Not that fish. Fish from the other side." And he would get the fish.

On the ocean side of Rongerik, sitting on the coral reef, there was a small island called **Jibedbō**. On this tiny bit of island lived an old man, **Lajibedbō**. He walked with a cane, coughed constantly, and had spit and snot in his beard. Whenever the *iroij* sailed off, Lajibedbō hobbled over to say good-bye.

"Watch over the *lejale*," the *iroij* always told him. He didn't trust the younger men of the island.

Whenever the canoes had disappeared from

**Jibedbō** JEE-ber-beuh

**Lajibedbō** lah-JEE-behr-beuh

182

sight, Lajibedbō disappeared into the bush. He would shake. He would shake until his old man skin came completely off. He would shake until he was a handsome young man.

*[Jorju paused and looked at me. He laughed, saying, "The same like you . . . handsome!"]*

The women all adored Lajibedbō. He was so perfect, so muscular and strong. They brought him food and coconuts. They searched his head for lice. He spent every moment with the *lejale* and the women of Rongerik. But it was never enough for the *lejale*. When the *iroij* returned, Lajibedbō had to step into the bush and become the old man again.

So one time, the *lejale* sent her husband looking for a fish from far, far to the north.

"Why not the fish here?" the *iroij* asked. "It's the same."

"Well," the *lejale* told him, "maybe I'm getting morning sickness."

"Oh," said the *iroij*. "Ooooh." He called his men together and told them to get the canoes ready.

Lajibedbō ambled over the reef again as the *iroij* and his men set sail. "Keep close watch," the *iroij* shouted to him.

"Okay," coughed out the old man, stepping into the bushes.

Now every chance she got, the *lejale* sent her husband far to the north. "It's the morning sickness." He would be gone for days at a time.

A time came, however, when the *iroij* had caught so many fish, the whole island couldn't finish them all. So the next day, when the *lejale* said she wanted fish from the north, the *iroij* was surprised. "We still have that fish."

"I want the kind from way out there," the *lejale* said.

"But this is . . . "

"You won't do this for me?" the *lejale* cried. "When I need fresh fish, the raw fish to eat?"

"It's true," thought the *iroij*. "The morning sickness is still there."

As the *iroij* sailed with his men, old man Lajibedbō changed into the handsome young man of the *lejale*'s dreams.

What the *lejale* didn't know was the *iroij* had jumped out of his canoe and secretly swum back to the island. As he snuck back to his house, he saw the young man Lajibedbō.

"Who is this man who's come to my island?" he wondered. Crawling through the bush he stumbled on the old-man skin. "That man is no good," he said to himself. "He's stolen my wife!" The *iroij* burned the old-man skin. He ran to his house and there he saw the *lejale* lying in the arms of the young Lajibedbō.

"You lied," the *iroij* shouted in anger. "You've never had morning sickness. You told me to go far away so you could be with that man."

The young Lajibedbō laughed hard. "You're the fool here."

"You're trying to steal my wife!" The *iroij* picked up his machete and tried to kill the young Lajibedbō. But Lajibedbō grabbed the machete, threw it far away, and punched the *iroij* until he was dead. The young man was so very happy, he cried out, "Ha ha ha ha ha ha, wonderful."

*Did you look on the other side? Because if you did you can see that foolishness is its own reward.*

# KAJKAKI

**Kajkaki**
  KAHJ-kah-kee

**Bok** bohk

*raj* [rahj] whales

*Bwebwenato in Ujae. This story is from the island of **Bok**, in Ujae Atoll.*

An old woman of **Bok** could sing with the *raj*. Her son, Kajkaki, built her a big house so she could be close to the whales. Every night the old woman sang her whales to shore. Every night she sang them home to sleep.

> *You fill the sea, my pets, you fill the sea.*
> *Come now, jump out, my pets, jump till you're with me.*

So many whales always came, the oldest whales had to sleep on the roof of the house. From his rooftop bed, the oldest of the whales sang through the night, lulling his brothers and sisters, and the old woman and her son, to a peaceful sleep.

> *Together we fill our home, oh sleep please sleep.*
> *Our home is full, let us sleep.*

When morning came, the old woman would sing the whales awake so they could return to the water to feed themselves.

> *Fill the sea, my pets, go fill the sea.*

*It's time to leave, my pets, leap till you fill the sea.*

One morning, after the whales had left, the old woman asked Kajkaki to sail south in search of a tender fish she could feed her whales.

As Kajkaki set sail, a chief from the nearby island of **Ib** watched. As Kajkaki disappeared into the horizon, this chief called two of his men. "I want that thing, that floating tree," he told them. There weren't many canoes then, and this chief wanted Kajkaki's.

The two men swam and swam and swam and swam from sunrise till the sun nearly set. They swam all the way from Ib to Bok. They arrived very tired.

The old woman sat alone on the sand at a place called **Lōiroij**. She sang her nightly song:

*You fill the sea, my pets, you fill the sea.*
*Come now, jump out my pets, jump till you're with me.*

As the whales leapt ashore and squeezed themselves into the house, the Ib men huddled in the bushes and watched, wide-eyed.

"There's too much magic here," one said, shivering.

"What magic?" asked the braver of the two.

"The man rides a floating tree," the first answered. "And those big fish."

The brave one said, "Never mind that. Come on."

In the distance, the oldest whale chanted:

*Together we fill our home, oh sleep please sleep.*
*Our home is full, let us sleep.*

**Ib** ihb

**Lōiroij** leuh-ih-ROHJ

187

The Ib men neared the house. They saw a big, scraped-out tree. "Mmmmmm! Incredible!" the braver of the two cried.

"Magic," whispered the frightened one.

"What about that?" the brave one said, pointing to the huge house.

"I wish that was mine," answered the other.

"We'll take it all."

"This too?" said the frightened one, standing in a beautiful garden.

"Oh, yes," said the brave one. "Now let's sleep."

The two dug a hole under the canoe and fell asleep. They never saw the old woman, but she had heard them talking. The old woman sang softly to her distant son:

> *Kajkaki Kajkaki ie,*
> *Kajkaki Kajkaki oh.*

'We're trying to sleep," the oldest whale called to her. "You're making too much noise."

But the old woman continued:

> *Kajkaki Kajkaki ie,*
> *Kajkaki Kajkaki oh.*

The whales called out for her to be quiet. The old woman chanted on, waking the Ib men. Those men set fire to the house. The woman cried to the whales,

> *Fill the sea, my pets, go fill the sea.*
> *It's time to leave, my pets, leap till you fill the*
> *sea.*

The whales leapt to the ocean. The Ib men dug

up the old woman's garden. The old woman called
to her son,

> *Kajkaki Kajkaki ie,*
> *Kajkaki Kajkaki oh.*

But Kajkaki didn't hear. He was too far away.
The Ib men took all the taro.

The old woman chanted stronger,

> *Kajkaki Kajkaki ie,*
> *Kajkaki Kajkaki oh.*
> *Momman ie ruo ne, ilo boken enem im Ib.*

> Kajkaki Kajkaki *ie,*
> Kajkaki Kajkaki *oh.*
> The two men from the small island called Ib.

Kajkaki heard a little something. He stopped
fishing. Meanwhile the Ib men grabbed the canoe.
The old woman continued,

> *Rōbla rekōnak, ene enem Ib ener.*
> *Rōbla rekōnak, wa in wan Ib waer.*
> *Rōbla rekōnak, el in elen Ib eler.*

> This island is taken by the Ib people,
> This canoe is taken by the Ib people,
> Everything on the island is taken by the
> Ib people.

Kajkaki finally heard his mother. He chanted
to his canoe,

> *Annoñ annoñ annoñ, ooooooooo.*

Paddle, paddle, paddle, ooooooooo.

The Ib men ran oceanside of Bok, but they had never paddled a canoe. It broke.

Kajkaki's canoe sped to Bok. He saw his mother there, crying for her pets. The Ib men leapt into Kajkaki's canoe and rode off, screaming his chant. Kajkaki couldn't go after them, since all his canoes were gone.

The old woman called to the whales, but they had dove deep into the ocean to escape the Ib men.

*If you visit Bok today you can see whales far off the shore, singing and playing and watching to see if the men are trying to chase them.*

# JALUIT

## NEILEM BANEB

**Neilem Baneb**
NEH-lem bah-NEB

**Jabwor** jahb-OHR

***ejjōb aō***
[EJ-jeuhb aeuh]
a kind of baseball, using only hands and a Marshallese woven ball

***bu ball*** [BOO ball]
a marble game

At first it was difficult finding someone to share stories on Jaluit. The local health assistant, or "doctor," tried hard to find someone to share a story. Finally, Neilem Baneb agreed, but only because my traveling companion, Sylvia, was related to her. Even Sylvia didn't know that. But that's how it goes in the Marshall Islands.

Neilem was born in Jaluit, Jaluit, but lived with her grandparents on the next island over, **Jabwor**. As a young girl Neilem played with her younger sister and other girls around the very area where she told me stories. They played ***ejjōb aō***. She also liked to play hopscotch and a game with marbles they call ***bu ball***. At the age of five, Neilem started doing chores around the house, including soaking the husks of coconuts in the ocean so her grandfather could make sennit from them. Her grandmother taught her how to make mats: collecting the pandanus leaves, removing their thorns, drying them over a fire, rolling, softening, and weaving them.

Just a few months after she started fourth grade, World War II came to her island. She and her grandparents were the first to run across the reef from Jabwor Island to Jaluit Island. As they made their way, however, they came upon a Japanese soldier pointing his gun right at them. Her uncle, who worked with the Japanese, asked the soldier to let them join Neilem's parents. The soldier did. The scariest part of the whole ordeal, she said, was the sound of guns and bombs. Even though her family hid underground, she could hear those sounds. Her parents told her to pray. Neilem said all she could think about was whether they were going to live or not.

**NEILEM BANEB**

# LŌMANJIRILIK, THE DEMON-BOY

**Lōmanjirilik**
  leuh-mahn-jih-
  REE-lihk

**Bokilañ** BOHK-ee-
  lahng

**Lōmanjideb** leuh-
  MAHN-jih-reb

**Bokidik**
  boh-KIH-drihk

**Lodiren**
  loh-RIH-ren

*anidreb*
  [ah-NEE-reb]
  a game similar
  to footbag

*I'll start the story now. It's from Jaluit, Jaluit.*

In a small village called **Bokilañ**, the old lady **Lōmanjideb** lived with her son, a half-demon. He treated her badly, ordering her to do this and that for his own happiness. Whenever she asked for help, that demon-boy Lōmanjirilik laughed at her and did the opposite. Once, just to annoy her, the half-demon boy took off to the other side of the island.

On the other side, in **Bokidik** village, the girl **Lodiren** lived with her father, the *iroij*. She loved to play *anidreb* with the girls of the village.

When Lōmanjirilik reached Bokidik village he saw Lodiren playing and singing:

> *Lōmanjideb itom drebet anidreb ie neju,*
> *jolok ñan liji-en jolok ñan liji-eo,*
> *jolok ñan jikko weo jikko eo jikko drebiji.*

> Lōmanjideb come and take my *anidreb*,
> Throw it to that girl, throw it to this girl,
> Throw it to the hated one and that hated one catch it.

Lōmanjirilik marched right in. The girls ran off, screaming. The demon-boy chased them all the way to the village, but stopped when he saw the people. He stamped off home.

"Where did you go?" his mother asked. "It's really late."

"Never mind about that," he shouted at her, and disappeared into the house.

The following day Lōmanjirilik set off early. When he reached Bokidik, Lodiren was already playing. The demon-boy leapt right out of the bushes and gave chase. The girls reached the village before him. Lōmanjirilik stormed home. His mother felt his anger that night.

For three days Lōmanjirilik tried to catch Lodiren. For three days the girls escaped him. Then one day Lodiren slipped as she ran. Lōmanjirilik grabbed her and carried her home.

At Bokilañ, Lōmanjirilik tied the girl up and hid her in the cookhouse. His mother asked, "What are you putting in there?"

"Nothing," he told her. "Start the fire. I'm hungry."

The demon-boy climbed a breadfruit tree. While he dropped breadfruit, his mother looked into the cookhouse.

"Where did you come from?" she asked the girl.

"We were just playing," the frightened Lodiren said.

The demon-boy shouted from the tree, "Mother!"

"I'm bringing the basket now," Lōmanjideb called. Then she said to the girl, "This is what I need you to do . . . "

She untied Lodiren and gave her four *lot*, each with something inside.

*lot* [laht]
hollow coconuts

"Mother!" the demon-boy screamed, climbing quickly down the tree.

"Run now," his mother said, "but don't try to outrun him—throw the *lot*."

"Mother," Lōmanjirilik demanded, "what are you doing in the cookhouse!"

Lodiren ran. Lōmanjirilik screamed. The girl ran harder, but the demon-boy hurried after her. Lodiren threw the first *lot*. It broke open and black ants came pouring out.

"My pets! You've stolen my pets!" He gathered them into the *lot* and sprinted after her.

Lodiren threw the next *lot* just as she passed across Jaluit Island. Cockroaches flew out.

"Raaaa! You'll kill them all!" he yelled, gathering them up. "I'm going to do the same for you!" He was becoming more demon than he had ever been.

When Lodiren neared Bokidik, she threw the next. Small red ants leapt out.

"My favorites!" Lōmanjirilik screeched. "I'm really going to get you, and my mother, too!"

The demon-boy leapt into the air. Lodiren screamed. The men of her village came running. Lōmanjirilik came down on top of Lodiren, but the men grabbed him and killed the demon-boy of Jaluit.

Lodiren and her father the *iroij* invited Lōmanjideb to live with them at Bokidik.

# THE FLYING WIFE

*Jaluit women sometimes must fly. This is why.*

A couple had several sons. They lived on a small island called **Ewo** in Jaluit Atoll. Another couple lived with several girls at a village called **Elibobo**.

**Ewo** EH-woh

**Elibobo** eh-lee-BOH-boh

**Lōmanluklok** leuh-MAHN-luhk-lohk

One day one of the boys, **Lōmanluklok**, walked across the reef from Ewo to Jaluit Island. He saw the girls collecting coconut crabs.

He called the youngest over. "Bring your oldest sister so we can have a date."

When she came, Lōmanluklok asked if she'd marry him. The young woman said, "I like it, but I have to wait to ask my mama and papa. They have gone fishing on the island across the lagoon."

"I'll come back tomorrow then."

The young woman told him, "No, you have to wait three days."

Lōmanluklok said, "No, I'll return tomorrow."

"Better to wait three days so I can talk to Mama and Papa."

But Lōmanluklok refused to listen. He returned the next day.

The young woman's parents asked, "Why is he here?"

"He wants to stay with me."

"Okay, but we don't want to hear if there are problems."

The young woman asked Lōmanluklok, "My parents want to know if you have a wife already."

"No," he lied. He stayed there in Elibobo village, even though he had a wife and kids on Ewo.

Days and days and days passed. One morning, while the youngest daughter played at the end of the island, she saw something flying. "What kind of a person is that?"

The stranger flew all the way to the house of her sister and Lōmanluklok.

"Lōmanluklok, Lōmanluklok!" the flying stranger cried.

"What is that?" asked the oldest daughter.

The youngest came running, "Look, look, sister! A flying woman!"

"Lōmanluklok," the woman in the sky cried, "this is where you've gone?"

"Yes," answered Lōmanluklok. "And I'm here to stay."

The flying woman saw Lōmanluklok's new wife and was jealous. She was very beautiful.

The flying woman fainted from the sky. The youngest girl ran to her, but Lōmanluklok just said, "Go home, for my new wife is pregnant."

The woman flew home. She was so sad she wouldn't eat, she wouldn't feed her children, wouldn't talk or anything. The flying woman was so very sad she died.

*This is why the people there are so jealous and won't cooperate with others. The girls' hearts break easily. And if they see someone with their husband or boyfriend, they fly.*

# NAMDRIK

## JIA HISAIAH
## IBAN EDWIN

Jia Hisaiah and Iban Edwin were partners. They created songs and dances for a dance group they led for years on Namdrik, which was considered one of the treasures of Marshall Islands culture. In 1992, Jia and Iban and their group represented the Marshalls at the Festival of Pacific Arts in Rarotonga, Cook Islands.

**Jia Hisaiah** JEE-ah
heye-SAY-ee-ah

**Iban Edwin**
ee-BAHN ED-
ween

### Iban Edwin

Iban Edwin was the dance master of the team. Iban created most of the dances you would see from Namdrik.

He lived with his grandmother and grandfather in Ebon Atoll from the time he was one year old. "I listened to stories told by a man named **Lamare**. He always told stories at his house. Kids always went to his house to listen, and he'd tell a story, anytime."

Iban attended Japanese school for a few years until the war came to the Marshalls. After the war Iban moved to Namdrik Atoll and started creating

**Lamare**
LAH-mah-reh

songs for the Christmas celebration. About the same time he joined up with Jia.

In 1994/95, I teamed up with Jia and Iban to create a play based on stories and dances from Namdrik. Iban told me, "When I heard there was an American guy coming to Namdrik to get stories from me I was thinking, Why? What is he going to do with these stories? Then when you brought me and Jia to Hawai'i, and I saw the play you made from them, it made me think about my grandfather. Watching the play was like listening to my grandfather. It was really good because it meant to me the stories are still alive.

"I thought maybe we couldn't hold on to our story, but you came to our island and we worked together to keep our culture and customs alive so we won't lose them."

## Jia Hisaiah

Jia Hisaiah was born in Namdrik. At nineteen he started creating songs. But at twenty, the Japanese took him to work on Jaluit. Jia said, "[When the war started] I went with a bunch of Marshallese to go to the island of **Boknake**. At nighttime we went and stole a small Japanese boat and we paddled to

**Boknake**
bohk-NAH-keh

Boknake. We didn't use lights to cross the lagoon, but there was shelling and we could see just fine. We couldn't talk. In Boknake, we hid underground when the American planes came over. At nighttime we danced. The first time I made a dance was in Boknake during the war."

When the war was over, Jia started creating Christmas songs and dances in Namdrik. He met Iban at that time. When they formed their dance group, Iban created the songs and dances and Jia taught them to the group. The group became known through a local competition. As Jia says, "A competition came up in Majuro. We went and danced there. We sold tickets and made money. And the [Marshall Islands] president's brother was there. We performed for him. Later, another chief invited us to perform for the celebration of his new house. In 1992 they told us to get ready for the Festival of Arts in Rarotonga. And when we came back, we were invited to dance at the opening of the capitol.

"Then there was this American guy that we call Letao, and he told us to get ready to go to Hawai'i with the dance and the song. We went to Honolulu to show the dance.

"It was really good to see what you did with that play. The people in the Marshalls almost forget the custom and when they see this they will feel that the stories should never be forgotten. All the Marshallese should see this so that they feel good about their custom. See this play and learn from it. Remember."

Jia died in 1998.

# JOLUKWOR

*Namdrik Atoll is two small islands. The bigger island is shaped like a* lei *of flowers. It's called Namdrik. The smaller island is like the bow tying the* lei *together. It's called* **Madmad***. No one lives on the tiny island of Madmad anymore.*

**Jolukwor**
JOH-luhk-woor

**Madmad**
MAHR-mahr

*Etto im etto* . . . Long and long time past . . .

There was an old man named Jolukwor, who lived alone on Namdrik. If he fell ill, there was no one to take care of him.

One day a sore appeared on his right thigh. The sore grew so painful Jolukwor could hardly walk. The pain grew so intense the old man was unable to sleep. He rolled about on his mat, moaning and holding tight to his leg. Finally, in the dark of the night, a sharp pain exploded throughout his body.

A voice beside him spoke. "Father, are you all right?"

Jolukwor opened his eyes to see two girls sitting near him.

"Who . . . ?" the old man stuttered.

"We're your daughters," one replied.

The sore on his leg was gone.

"I have two daughters." The old man smiled. "Two beautiful daughters." He reached out to hug them, but his leg still bothered him.

"Stay there, father," one told him. "We're here to help you."

"What a beautiful sound," Jolukwor said. "Father."

Even with his new daughters' help, however, the old man's leg continued to get worse. Jolukwor called his daughters to him.

"I'm going to die," he told them. "When I do, please make me a grave under your window. After you've buried me, go to my two mothers on Madmad."

The next morning Jolukwor died. His two daughters did as he wished, burying him beneath their window. The two then took their father's canoe and paddled across the lagoon to Madmad Island.

On the island, the two had to cut their way through thick bushes. At the edge of the thick bush, the girls discovered a swamp. A small house stood nearby.

The girls approached the quiet house. Unknown to them, two pairs of eyes followed their every move. As the girls knocked on the door, the eyes squinted. As the girls peeked into the window, the eyes opened wide. As the girls climbed into the house, the eyes disappeared deep into the bush.

The girls found very little inside. "*Iakwe,*" they called into the silence.

The door creaked open. The girls looked. Two very old women grabbed them. The old women locked the two in a room.

As darkness fell over the island the girls huddled together, afraid of what these old women, these demons, might do. In the middle of the night they heard the front door open. All night long the girls listened to the front door opening and closing many times.

At first light, the girls peeked out through a crack in the door. They saw a large pile of bananas, taro, breadfruit, and coconuts.

"What's happening out there?" the younger girl asked.

"They're preparing to cook," her sister said.

The door to the room opened and food flew in.

"Eat, eat, eat, eat, and eat," the old women told the girls. "Make yourselves fat."

"Cook . . . what?" the younger girl asked.

The sounds of the old women digging an earth oven seeped through the walls.

"Us," said the older.

The door opened. The old witches stood there, mouths open wide.

The girls called out, "Father, Father, why did you send us to these demons? Father?"

The old lady demons opened their mouths wide, wide, wider. The girls cried again, "Father, Father, why did you send us to these demons? They're going to eat us, Father, Father Jolukwor."

One of the lady demons stopped. "Listen," she said to her demon sister. "Listen!"

The girls sang out, "Father, Father Jolukwor, why did you send us to your demon-mothers? They're going to have us for supper, Father, Father Jolukwor."

The demons turned to each other. "The girls are calling our son Jolukwor."

The old women grabbed the girls. They screamed even louder, "Father Jolukwor!"

The old women said, "Jolukwor is your father?"

"Yes," the younger girl cried. "He had a boil. It erupted and we came out."

The old women hugged and kissed the two girls.

"Our father died," said the older. "But he told us to come and look for you."

The old women hugged the girls tighter and cried. "We're so very sorry for the way we treated you, our daughters."

The next day they sailed to Jolukwor's house. They found a banana tree growing from the grave, the very first *jolukwor* banana tree.

*The swamp still sits in the middle of Madmad. A small hole is all that remains of Jolukwor's grave. But the* jolukwor *banana grows all over Namdrik and the rest of the Marshall Islands.*

**Jia Hisaiah and Iban Edwin**

# UOM AND TAK

*Etto im etto* . . . Long and long time past . . .

**Uom** ohm

**Tak** tahk

Tak the fish bragged and bragged and bragged. All the time he bragged. Tak the fish bragged he could swim faster than the wind. Tak the fish bragged he could swim faster than the waves. Tak the fish bragged he could swim faster than any creature in the sea.

Uom the crab got tired of listening to Tak the fish. "If we raced, you'd lose," Uom said to Tak.

Tak the fish jumped about the water, spouting, "No way a crawly crab could ever beat the fastest fish in the sea."

"Maybe," Uom said. "Wanna race?"

"I'd make a fool of you," Tak said.

Uom shrugged, "That means I win."

"No you don't!" snapped Tak. "We race tomorrow."

All the creatures of the lagoon heard about the race. Every one of them was sure who'd win, and they argued the day away waiting for the big event.

Tak swam about, showing off. He'd never had such an audience.

"Did you ever see such a fine fish as me? Did you ever see such a fast fish as me?"

As the gossip and bragging wore on, Uom the crab swam along the lagoon gathering his brothers, sisters, and cousins. "Tomorrow's the race," he told them. "Hide near each island, right at the edge of the lagoon. And here's what you do . . . "

The race day dawned. Tak and Uom met at Kaben Island.

"Think you're ready?" asked Tak the fish.

"Let's race," answered Uom the crab.

Tak swam off fast. He swam, swam, and swam until he couldn't see Uom. Tak the fish laughed and laughed. He called out, "Uom, oh, Uom, where are you?" To Tak's surprise he heard a voice in front of him.

"Oh, I'm here," the crab voice said. "I'm still here."

"There?" Tak swam faster. He didn't see Uom anywhere, so called out again, "Uom, oh, Uom, where are you?"

Far ahead of him a crab voice called, "Oh, I'm here. I'm still here."

Tak spurred himself on. He didn't even stop to call the next time, "Uom, oh, Uom . . ."

"Oh, I'm still here," the crab voice called, still far ahead.

Tak pushed himself harder and faster. But every time he called, the crab voice called from just beyond—island after island, all along the lagoon, from Kaben all the way to Tarawa Island, the end of the race.

When Tak arrived at Tarawa, he flopped onto the shore completely exhausted. He looked up, and there sat Uom the crab, patiently waiting. "What took you so long, fish?"

Tak's mouth just opened and closed, without a sound. He slowly slipped into the water and died.

*This story says we must work together to win. Don't be the braggart who cares only for himself.*

JIA HISAIAH AND IBAN EDWIN

# THE REEF CAME TO BE IN SORROW

*Etto im etto . . .* Long and long time past . . .

A man went fishing. A man named **Bejbejinna**.

Bejbejinna sailed out from Namdrik Island. The wind sent his **kōrkōr** flying over the dark blue water.

*sssh-Pbish! sssh-Pbish! sssh-Pbish!* Three dark spots shot out from a white-tipped wave.

"Ah, *jojo*," said Bejbejinna.

The flying fish skimmed the whitecaps, their winglike fins riding Bejbejinna's wind. He dropped his **emjak** and folded down his **ujelā mañ**.

Bejbejinna caught fish and fish and fish, many fish. "When everyone sees these *jojo*," he thought, "there'll be mouths watering all over the island. Filled-up stomachs for days and days." He laughed to himself. "And days."

Bejbejinna raised his small *ujelā*. He pointed his *kōrkōr* straight for the island. His excitement grew as the wind filled his sail. What could be better for a Namdrik **dri-eñod** than to return with plenty of fish to share?

Because *dri-eñod* shared their catch with the island community, everyone sang for the fishermen as they sailed onto the shore. Island custom held that the people celebrated the fresh-caught fish and the men who caught them. So when Bejbejinna sailed within sight of Namdrik's shore, he scooped

**Bejbejinna**
  bej-BEJ-een-nah

**kōrkōr**
  [KEUHR-keuhr]
  small canoe

**emjak** [EM-jahk]
  rock anchor

**ujelā mañ**
  [OO-jeh-leye
  mahng]
  a sail

**dri-eñod**
  [ree-eng-OHR]
  fisherman

the piled fish into his arms, ready to join the song and celebration.

But no one was waiting for him. No one stood at the shore.

The wind dropped his *ujelā*. The small *kōrkōr* stopped, dead on the waves. Bejbejinna stepped out of his canoe into the shallow water. Sorrow washed over him as he stared at the empty shore. "How could it be?" he whispered. One by one the fish slipped from his arms into the ice-colored sea.

Bejbejinna collapsed into the shallows. The ocean wrapped its gentle waves over his body. Bejbejinna's sorrow, Bejbejinna's life, slowly ebbed away with the tide.

Bejbejinna died there in the water, near the empty shore of Namdrik.

The tide carried his sorrow, lifting and tumbling, around the island. Slowly, as the waves pushed and patted, the sorrow of the *dri-eñod* Bejbejinna sank into the sand, becoming as hard and rough as his *emjak*.

**bedbed** [BED-bed]
newborn coral
reef

When the people of the island did come looking for Bejbejinna, a funny little thing happened. As they waded into the shallow water, each and every one of them slipped on the hardened ground. Some fell. The **bedbed** bit at the people so they wouldn't forget.

> *Wait for the* dri-eñod.
> *Celebrate them at the shore.*
> *Remember the island customs,*
> *The sorrow of Bejbejinna.*

JIA HISAIAH AND IBAN EDWIN

# THE BIG CANOE AND THE TEENY-TINY BEACH BIRD

*Etto im etto* . . . Long and long time past . . .

All the birds of the Marshall Islands lived on the island of Aelōñlaplap. And the king of all the birds was Kako the rooster. More than anything, King Kako loved singing his song while sailing along in his favorite canoe. "Kako! Kako! Kako!"

One day, however, **Kako** decided his canoe wasn't big enough. "I need a BIG canoe," he crowed to all the birds of the island. "Build me one!"

**Kako** [KAH-koh]
A *kako* is a rooster.

At once every bird began pecking, pawing, poking, and plopping pieces of wood together for the canoe. When they finished, Kako glanced at the canoe and clucked, "Build it bigger."

So all the birds ran about pecking, pawing, poking, and plopping until they'd built an even bigger canoe. Kako hardly even glanced at it before he shouted, "Bigger! Bigger!"

The birds flew back to work, pecking, pawing, poking, and plopping till the canoe was big enough to hold every single bird on the island, with room enough for Kako's house, too.

Kako tilted his head back and forth, clicking and clucking. Every bird held its breath. Kako puffed out his feathery chest and sang, "KAKO! That's the biggest canoe I ever saw!"

All the birds leaped and laughed and twirled and twittered. "Kako! Kako! Kako!" they shouted, in praise of their king's brilliance.

King Kako strutted about, making a grand show of climbing aboard his shiny, new, BIG canoe. He stood in the middle of the canoe all puffed and proud and crowed.

Two birds skittered up to the canoe and gave it a big push. "Ebōel li ke wa in!" they chanted.

The canoe didn't budge one inch.

Kako ruffled his feathers and crowed once more. "Ebōel li! Push the canoe!"

Several more birds jumped to his side. "Ebōel li ke wa in!" they chanted, pushing with all their strength.

The canoe settled deeper into the wet sand.

King Kako started dancing about the canoe and screaming at the top of his lungs, "Ebōel li, Ebōel li, Ebōel li!!! PUSH PUSHPUSHPUSH!!!!"

More and more birds flew to the canoe, but no matter how hard they tried, Kako's big canoe just wouldn't move off the sandy beach.

In the middle of all that screaming and chanting a teeny-tiny voice peeped, "This is coconuts."

Every bird fell quiet. Kako cocked his head from side to side. "Who said that?" he whispered.

No one answered.

King Kako strutted from stem to stern. "Is every bird here?"

"Every bird," they answered together.

"Then why isn't my beautiful canoe moving?!" Kako called for more wings to push his big, Big, BIG canoe. The birds pushed. The canoe sat. Kako crowed and crowed until every bird on the island was pushing and shoving and heaving and grunting. But the canoe and the birds just sank deeper and deeper into the sand.

The tiny voice cried out again, "Coconuts. This is coconuts!"

Kako beat his wings and shouted till his comb turned blue. "Who Keeps Saying That?!?"

All the birds hid their heads under their wings, shaking.

The tiny voice peeped, "It's me. It's Me!"

An empty coconut shell flipped over. There stood a teeny-tiny beach bird with legs no bigger than breadfruit stems. Kako leaned over till his beak almost touched the sand.

"It's you?" asked King Kako. "You have the big mouth?"

"I'm **Annung**. Annung," the tiny bird said, nodding its head. A small wave knocked the tiny bird over and sent him tumbling down the beach. The other birds laughed as he tried to outrun the next wave.

**Annung**
AHN-nuhng

Kako laughed hardest. "Kako Kako Kako Kako!"

Annung covered his tiny ears. "Too much noise. Too much noise!"

Kako stopped laughing. He squinted at little Annung.

"I'm the King!" Kako cried. "I can make all the noise I want. KAKO!"

"But your noise can't move the canoe," said the tiny beach bird.

"And what can?" Kako asked, laughing. "You?"

"That's me. That's me," Annung answered, flapping his tiny wings and strutting about like the king himself.

Every bird started laughing, but the rooster quieted them with an angry "KAKO!"

"Too much noise," Annung peeped.

"Okay, Chief Too-much-noise! Push the canoe," Kako said, and he climbed aboard.

Annung strutted from stem to stern, making fun of King Kako as the waves washed farther up the beach.

"Wait," said the king. He gestured for two birds to join him in the canoe. "Now push," Kako ordered.

Again the tiny bird started strutting. "Look at me! I'm the king of all the birds!" The waves washed closer and closer to the canoe.

"Wait," Kako cried, and told all the others to jump onto his huge canoe. "Now push," he said, clucking and chuckling at the teeny, tiny bird.

At that moment a wave washed right under the big canoe. And at that moment, tiny Annung pushed. *Ebōel li ke wa in!*"

The canoe slipped off the beach. The king and all the birds clucked and crowed in disbelief. The teeny-tiny bird had launched the canoe!

Annung laughed and danced on the beach as the waves carried Kako and the BIG canoe out onto the ocean. "High tide. High tide!" Annung sang. "What a coconut he is. He never saw the high tide!"

# REEF EYES

*Etto im etto* . . . Long and long time past . . .

On the tiny island of Namdrik two young girls played tricks on everyone and everything. The two sat in coconut trees and dropped big brown nuts on anyone walking by. The two greased the ceiling of their house with coconut oil so tiny lizards scuttling by plopped to the floor. The two grabbed the legs of sleeping pigs, making them squeal till the whole island awoke from the noise.

Their parents scolded them. "Stop playing tricks on everyone and everything," they said. "You're going to get in trouble you can't get out of."

The girls never listened. Instead they decided to play their biggest trick ever. This is what happened.

The chief of the island paddled in from the ocean one morning with a big load of fish. He piled all his fish in front of his house, then went in to take a short rest. When he came back out, the fish were gone.

"What happened to my fish?" he shouted.

A burst of giggles rustled the trees above him. Looking up through the leaves he saw the two girls. "It was you two!"

"We never saw your fish," said the first.

"We're just collecting coconuts," answered the other.

"I know you two. I know you have my fish," he yelled. "I want them back right now."

"Right now?" the two girls asked together, then smiled.

"Right this very moment," he told them.

The two girls shook the tree. Fish rained down. So many fish rained down, the chief had to run into his house to keep from getting buried. But he had caught a big bunch of fish. The fish kept raining and raining until the roof of his house caved in!

The two girls slid down the tree and skipped off, laughing. The chief pulled himself out of the pile of fish and house. He wasn't laughing. He let out a furious roar.

The girls heard the chief roar. The two got scared. They cried out to everyone and everything, even little lizards and pigs, but no one came to help them. So they took off running, with the chief roaring and running right after them.

The girls ran all the way to the very end of the island. There, at the edge of the reef, sat a huge clam with its mouth wide open, basking in the sun. They could hear the chief's roar coming closer. The two girls leapt into the mouth of the clam and slammed it shut. Just four wide eyes peeked through the tiny crack as the girls waited nervously for the furious chief.

The chief roared right up to the reef. But as hard as he tried he never found those two. And to this day the girls still hide there. That's why in the Marshall Islands the clam is called *mejenwōd*, reef eyes.

# LELI

*Etto im etto . . . Bwebwenato in Namdrik*

Long and long time past . . . A story of Namdrik Atoll

Every day Leli's mother went with him as he practiced his fighting skills. She stayed by Leli. The men of the island always laughed at the sight of Leli and his mother.

**Leli** LEH-lee

"I want to fight," Leli told his mother one time. "I'm strong."

"But where is your strength?" his mother asked.

"I'm strong enough to fight," Leli said.

"You have to know where your strength comes from or you might use it all up," she told him.

"Well, tell me already." All Leli really wanted to do was fight, not talk.

"At the right time," was the only answer his mother would give.

"I want to know now," Leli demanded, but his mother left.

A day came when *Iroij* **Kaiju** called all the men of the island together.

**Kaiju** KEYE-joo

"Start building the war canoes. Prepare your weapons. When the wind calls, we sail to conquer the islands and warriors of Ebon!" he told them.

They all cheered and set to work. The whole island kept busy felling breadfruit trees, cutting logs, building, weaving the pandanus leaf sails, collecting feathers for the stern and coconut shells to scoop water out of the new canoes, *wallap*.

Everyone except Leli. The men wouldn't let him join in the work.

"*Letil bako*!" they called him. "Mama's boy! Mama's little boy! Like the little fish that clings to the shark."

Leli flew at them, angered at the teasing. But his mother held him back.

"Leli," his mother said as she grabbed his arm.

"There's the strong man, Leli!" the men teased, "Let your mother protect you! No, let your mother fight!"

"I'll go to war by myself!" he yelled back at them. "I could fell a breadfruit tree faster than any of you!"

No one paid much attention. They thought of Leli as a small man. Leli seemed so small because of too much anger.

"Your strength is being used up in anger," his mother told him.

But Leli wouldn't listen. "I'm as fierce and strong as any of them."

"You do have the strength and the fierceness. But a warrior can't let that fierceness burn him up," she said.

"But what do I do?" he shouted.

"Soon . . . " was all she said.

"Always *soon*! I want now!" Leli stomped off.

The men finished the canoes. *Iroij* Kaiju brought them together on the beach.

"The winds are calling," Kaiju cried. "Time for war!"

The men dressed in the mats of war. They gathered the weapons. As they set sail, Leli came running. "Wait! I'm coming, too!"

"We don't want that boy," the men told the *iroij*.

"He's too small to fight. Let Leli stay with his mother."

"Stop talking!" *Iroij* Kaiju shouted. "I like this man. He'll come in my canoe!"

No one could believe the honor the chief offered Leli.

"Dip the water out of my canoe," he said to Leli. "Scoop up the water, so the canoe won't sink."

"What?" said Leli. "I don't want to scoop water. I want to fight!"

"Someone has to dip the water for their chief," answered Leli's mother, joining them on the beach.

"I want to fight."

"When it's time," she said.

"You come too," Kaiju said to her. "You'll sit with Leli and me."

"What?!" burst out Leli.

All the men laughed. *"Letil bako!"*

"Launch the *wallap*," Kaiju called, and blew the conch shell.

Together the men paddled, paddled, paddled across the ocean, set to bring war to Ebon.

"Ebon!" shouted one of the men, pointing to the horizon

"Ebon, Ebon, Ebon!" the rest chanted in reply.

The Namdrik men slammed their canoes onto the sand. They guided the *iroij*'s canoe onto the beach.

"Don't bring Leli," they told *Iroij* Kaiju.

"Don't worry, he'll stay in my canoe," Kaiju said.

"Stay? But . . . " Leli started to say, but his mother held him back. Leli sat, humiliated, scooping water out of the canoe.

The warriors of Ebon heard the rumblings of the drum rolling in with the waves. A large mob spilled onto the beach whooping loudly, working themselves to a feverish fighting pitch.

"Ebon!" they cried, to rally their enthusiasm.

The Namdrik men answered the heated excitement. "Namdrik!"

The island warriors shouted, beating their shields with wooden spears and clubs, threatening the others.

Then the fight began.

Whooping and running, the Namdrik warriors chased the Ebon men across the tiny island, driving them back with their fierceness and strength. But the men from Ebon fought back and drove the Namdrik warriors back again. The Namdrik warriors were backed all the way to the reef.

The crafty old chief watched his warriors being forced onto the reef. He turned to Leli and asked, "What do you think?"

Leli said, "We have the stronger men, but they just run about, yelling. All their power and spirit is being used up. You can't win that way. Why can't they see what's happening?"

"It's the right time," Leli's mother said.

"Now?" asked Leli.

"You have the wisdom."

*moun* [moh-OON] magic used to make men brave

Leli's mother began to chant a *moun*. Her magic made Leli grow and become a huge man. He grew because he really wanted to fight. His spirit grew inside him and his fire burned bright. He became a giant from his wisdom.

"Here," Leli's mother said.

Leli took the arrows. He took a bow. His mother began a chant to let his spirit fly free.

*En to Leli*
*kenu ke na,*

*ilikin borlab*
*bar jet, bar jet moman!*

Leave the boat, my son,
Leap out
Kill, kill those  men!

Leli leapt out of the canoe. He sailed over his own men, over the warriors of Ebon. He flew all the way across the island, landing in the middle of the Ebon men. Leli immediately killed a whole lot of the warriors. He let fly his arrows, taking down even more. He dodged the spears the Ebon men threw at him, picking the spears up and hurling them back at the enemy.

This giant man soon had his enemies trapped at one end of the island. The Namdrik men rallied behind him. They fought beside him. Each man felt his fire burning pure as, together, they cleared Ebon of every warrior.

When they got back to Namdrik the *iroij* rewarded Leli.

"For your strength, fierceness, and wisdom in war and for leading us in the fighting I give you the tip of this arrow. This arrow is the island of **Madmad**." So the giant Leli leapt over to his new home and settled down to live, a bigger man and wiser, respected by all.

**Madmad** MAHR-mahr

JIA HISAIAH

# LETAO, THE CHIEF, THE CANOE

*Etto im etto . . . Bwebwenato in Letao*
Long and long time past . . . A story of Letao

The Majuro *iroij* built a beautiful new outrigger canoe decorated with feathers and ribbons. It was the fastest on the island. Letao wanted it.

So Letao built his own outrigger. He made it from a hard wood, heavy like iron. It wouldn't float, but Letao made sure it shined like the sun. When he finished, Letao dragged the heavy canoe to the lagoon. He set it on a high piece of coral, so it seemed to float.

As morning dawned, Letao sat making a little toy from the pandanus tree: little squares with a sweet coconut candy inside. Instead of the sweet candy, however, Letao filled the toys with sand.

The *iroij* ordered his beautiful canoe brought to the lagoon. A crowd gathered to watch the *iroij* sail about the lagoon in his swift canoe.

"Whose canoe is this?" the *iroij* said, noticing the shiny new outrigger.

Letao stepped out of the crowd. "Mine."

"Beautiful outrigger," said the *iroij*.

"You like it?" Letao asked.

"I like your canoe very, very, very much."

"I'll trade you," Letao answered, "for your canoe."

"Mine's pretty nice, too," the *iroij* said.

"I'll give you this coconut candy I made, too."

They traded. Letao jumped into the *iroij*'s canoe and quickly sailed off.

The *iroij* made a great show of getting ready to sail in his shiny new outrigger. His men loaded up the coconut candy. The *iroij* stepped into the outrigger. "Push the canoe," he ordered. The men pushed. The heavy outrigger sank right to the bottom with the *iroij* and all that sweet candy. The men dived in to get the candy. As they pulled it out, sand fell through their fingers.

"Catch that Letao!" the *iroij* screamed. "He's got my canoe!"

The men jumped into their canoes and shoved off after Letao.

Letao kicked up great piles of rocks from the bottom of the lagoon. The rocks landed near the men, forming a new piece of land that blocked them. But the men sailed around the new land and continued the chase.

Letao sailed to **Rongrong** Island. He landed and buried himself in the sand, leaving one knee sticking out like driftwood.

**Rongrong**
ROHNG-rohng

The *iroij*'s men landed. They couldn't see Letao anywhere. They tied their canoes to the driftwood and scattered across the island, looking for the man who had tricked their *iroij*. When the men disappeared from sight, Letao unburied himself. He untied the canoes from his leg and sent them afloat on the lagoon.

Letao paddled off. The men returned to shore in time to see him disappear over the ocean. Letao had tricked them again.

And Letao sailed to America. That's why the people there are so smart.

*When you go to Majuro, you can still see those rocks.*

JIA HISAIAH

# LETAO AND THE KIRIBATI CHIEF

*Etto im etto. . . . Bwebwenato in Letao*
Long and long time past. . . A story of Letao

Letao was running away. He'd played another trick on an *iroij*, a chief, of the Marshall Islands. Letao took his canoe and headed straight for Kiribati. When he landed, Letao met the *iroij* of that island. They became good friends. And, in good Kiribati custom, all the people of the island brought food for Letao and the *iroij*.

After eating and eating all that Kiribati food, Letao said to the *iroij*, "Let me make food for you and all the Kiribati people."

Letao told the people to collect a big pile of lava rocks, a big pile of hard wood, and a nice bundle of big leaves. "We'll dig an underground oven, an *um*," he told them.

They started a fire in the hole in the ground. They put the rocks in. When the rocks glowed, the people carried in the food, but Letao stopped them.

"Instead of all the food, let me get in," Letao said.

The Kiribati people's eyes popped in surprise.

"The *um* is hot, very hot," the *iroij* said.

"Never mind how hot," answered Letao. "Let me crawl in and then cover me with the leaves."

So they did. They waited and waited. For two hours they waited. Then they opened the *um* up.

Instead of a cooked Letao they uncovered plenty of well-cooked food!

The *iroij* nearly burst with excitement. "I want to do that! Let me be the food. Build another *um*!" he told his people.

"No, no, you can't do that, you're the *iroij*." It was Letao. He just appeared from somewhere. "It's my job to make the food for you."

Letao had them build another big *um* with more hard wood to make sure it would burn extremely hot. More big leaves were brought to cover it. When the *um* sizzled and popped, the people opened it up for Letao to crawl in. But Letao surprised them all. "Your turn now," he said to the *iroij*.

The *iroij* walked up to the red-hot *um*. He stopped and said to Letao, "It's very hot, my Marshallese friend."

"Never mind how hot," Letao said. "Just think of all the delicious food you'll be." Letao pushed the *iroij* inside.

"Now hurry up, hurry up!" Letao told the Kiribati people. "Cover it up."

They placed the leaves on top. Then they waited. They waited and waited. For two hours they waited. Then they reopened the *um*. What did the Kiribati people see? Not much food. In fact, no food at all. Under the leaves lay an *iroij*, well done.

The Kiribati people wanted to punish Letao, but he sailed off before they discovered the cooked *iroij*. He sailed all the way to America. That's why the people there are so smart.

**IBAN EDWIN**

# INEDREL AND THE WHITE BIRD

*Etto im etto* . . . Long and long time past . . .
I'm telling you a story from the island of Ebon.

**Inedrel**
IHN-eh-rehl

A young boy named Inedrel lived with his mother and his father, the *iroij*, the chief of Ebon. His mother liked to weave and sing for her son. The *iroij* danced to her music, pulling Inedrel along in his quick-stepped prancing until they all fell to the ground laughing. The only thing Inedrel liked better than the laughter was sitting with his parents to a meal of fresh-caught fish, breadfruit, and coconut on one of his mother's finely woven mats. Too soon, however, Inedrel's mother died. His father married again, and Inedrel lost more than just a mother.

The *iroij*'s new wife didn't sing. She spent her time eating the best of the *iroij*'s food. The *iroij* became so busy gathering food, he stopped dancing. And when this new family sat down to eat, Inedrel got only fishbones, the stem of the breadfruit, and the worst fish of each day's catch. In time, only two sat down to eat.

Alone, Inedrel spent more and more time trying to remember his mother.

"Why did you leave me?" he asked her fading image every day.

"What's that boy of yours doing, just sitting out there?" Inedrel's new mother asked the *iroij*.

"Inedrel. Inedrel!" his father called.

Inedrel jumped up and ran quickly into the house. The smell of the food his stepmother was preparing made his stomach start growling.

"I'm hungry, *jema*."

*jema* [JEH-mah]
father

"Get the canoe ready for your father," his stepmother barked. She didn't give him any food.

Together father and son pushed the canoe into the lagoon. As they paddled out, Inedrel's stepmother watched from the shore.

"Bring back lots of fish for me," she shouted after them.

When they returned that afternoon with a canoe full of wiggling fish, she was waiting.

"I have breadfruit soup waiting for you," she called to Inedrel's father. "You," she pointed at Inedrel, "can bring in the canoe and the fish."

Inedrel struggled to pull the canoe, heavy with fish, up onto the sand. He slowly gathered the fish and placed them in a large woven basket. As he emptied the last fish, his stepmother reappeared.

"Your father ate the soup. This is what's left." She dropped a breadfruit stem in the sand and walked away with the fish.

So it went for days and weeks.

"Inedrel! Wake up," his father called every morning.

"Inedrel, the canoe!" his stepmother shouted, dropping fishbones on the ground for him.

"Inedrel! Stay here. I'll check the fishtrap," his father said as he dived under the water.

Until one day, as Inedrel waited in the canoe for his father, a *kear* appeared. Floating down out of the clouds, the white bird circled near Inedrel, singing as she rode the breeze.

*kear* KEH-ahr

"Inedrel," the white bird called to him. "Inedrel."

*jinō* [JIH-neuh]
  mother

"*Jinō*?" whispered Inedrel, not believing what he was hearing. "Mother?"

"Inedrel, you're pale," the bird sang. "What have you been eating?"

"Only . . . only fishbones and the stems of breadfruits," Inedrel stammered.

"Is that all?" asked the white bird.

"Maybe, uh, sometimes the tiniest fish we catch."

The white bird flew high above the canoe. "Come. Now. With me."

*anij* [AH-neej]
  a spirit

"But, you're *anij*," Inedrel said. "I'm afraid."

The white bird swooped down to pick up her son. "*Kinji,*" she sang out, grabbing the boy with her beak.

*kinji* [KIHN-jee]
  pinch

"No," cried Inedrel, more scared than hurt.

"*Abji,*" she sang, as she pulled at his arm.

*abji* [AHB-jee]
  to grab

"Please," cried the boy, trying to hide himself in the canoe.

*kelok* [KEH-lohk]
  to fly

"*Kelok,*" she said, as she disappeared into the sky.

Inedrel began to cry.

The *iroij* came up out of the water. He dumped the last of the fish onto the floor of the canoe. "You're crying," he said to his son, as he pulled himself into the canoe.

"The . . . the . . . the . . . the spine of a fish hurt my hand," Inedrel lied, afraid of his father.

"Don't be touching these fish!" Inedrel's father was furious. "They belong to your stepmother. Now paddle back to shore."

For each of three days the white *kear* visited Inedrel.

"*Kinji,*" the *kear* sang out, grabbing her son.

"No," cried Inedrel.

"*Abji,*" the white bird sang.

228

"Please," begged the boy.

"*Kelok.*" And she disappeared into the sky.

For each of three days Inedrel began to cry.

"Inedrel! You're crying again," his father shouted, as he came up out of the water.

"The fish hurt my hand," he lied.

"I told you not to touch these fish! How can you be so dumb!"

On the third night, Inedrel was not even given a fishbone.

Tired of his son's lies and crying, Inedrel's father decided to spy on the boy. Instead of diving under the water, the *iroij* floated quietly near the canoe.

"Inedrel," the white bird sang.

That voice so startled the *iroij* he almost didn't see the bird start to carry his son away.

"*Kinji.*"

"No!" cried the *iroij*, and leapt into the canoe.

"*Abji.*"

"Stop!" Inedrel's father yelled, grabbing hold of his son.

"*Kelok.*"

The white bird and Inedrel floated out of the canoe, but the *iroij* pulled until Inedrel fell back into it. With a single flap of wings, the white bird disappeared.

From that day on, Inedrel's father tried to take better care of his son. He gave his son the best of fish, the richest breadfruit, and only the sweetest of the coconuts. Inedrel, however, never said a word.

"What's that boy of yours doing, ignoring how generous you are?" Inedrel's stepmother snapped. "The ungrateful . . . "

But the *iroij* ignored her. Instead he held up a diamond-shaped toy he'd made. His new wife walked off in a huff.

"Inedrel," the *iroij* called, his voice almost singing with excitement. "I made this for you."

Inedrel said nothing. He didn't even look. He just sat. His father's excitement died. The *iroij* laid the **limakak** next to Inedrel and ducked into the house.

**limakak**
[LEE-mah-kahk]
kite

A small lagoon breeze teased the kite, making it scramble across the crushed coral yard. The wind grabbed it and the *limakak* began to dance. The string wiggled across Inedrel's lap, pulling and tugging him up onto his feet. Inedrel rose with the kite. Inedrel started to run along the beach, pulled along by kite and wind. People gathered to watch. The boy was dancing with the kite, singing to all the people who stood, staring.

*Limakak eo e kar ie nak to.*
*Roj aluluje nejio!*
*Tujeljel ion, takojeljel irok.*
*Lan ie jat ie tu, tujeljel.*

My kite is flying, leaping and playing with the breeze.
Everyone sees it fly!
Tumbling down, it snaps right back to the clouds.
A strong wind blows, dancing it across the sky.

"What's all that noise out there?" his stepmother yelled from the house. "Hey, look at your boy," she called to the *iroij*. "Where's he disappearing to?"

Inedrel's father threw open a window. "No," he cried. "No. Inedrel!" He ran out of the house, calling his son's name over and over.

Inedrel saw his mother near the end of the island. "*Jinō*! I want to fly with you. I do." The kite

picked him up off the ground, carrying him between the trees where his mother had been but a moment before.

Inedrel's father watched as the coconut palms swallowed up his son. The *iroij* ran faster, shouting to his son to stop. As he reached the end of the island, however, Inedrel was gone.

His father searched all over where he saw them disappear. Pushing aside trees and branches, he cried, "Where did you go? Where did you go?"

Two voices echoed, "Here we are. Here we are."

The *iroij* began to dig, following the echoes, searching desperately for his son.

Above him, past the tops of the trees, a white bird flew up through the clouds, a young boy beside her carried along by a magical kite.

The *iroij* kept digging. The rocks in the ground scratched and cut his hands, but he wouldn't stop digging. He dug and dug so many holes on Taka Island looking for his son. He dug and dug until he lay down and died.

A kite floated down near him, landing in the water. It became the small island **Dridri**.

**Dridri** REE-ree

*Dridri is shaped like a kite. The holes still exist on **Taka** Island. Now remember what I've told. We should never forget.*

**Taka** TAH-kah

**Iban Edwin**

# ELLICE ISLAND RIMENANUWE

*This story is from Ellice Island, about a* rimenanuwe *who introduced* **toto** *fishing.*

*Etto im etto* . . . Long and long time past . . .

One man from Ellice used to go fishing using a bamboo fishing pole. He would catch the ***mōn*** fish.

One day, while he was fishing he had to struggle hard. He pulled and the fish pulled; up and down went the line. The third time he pulled the line, he thought he had caught the fish, but instead he had caught a *rimenanuwe*, a little person. He immediately threw away his bamboo and ran off.

But the *rimenanuwe* called to him, "Come back here. I'm not a demon; I'm just a person who lives under the water."

The Ellice man stopped and turned around. He didn't say anything, just looked and wondered, Is that really a person? The Ellice man went back to the *rimenanuwe*.

The *rimenanuwe* told him, "I'll teach you how to do a special kind of fishing that we'll call *toto*." The *rimenanuwe* asked the Ellice man to show him how he fished. The *rimenanuwe* laughed at him and showed him a new way, a way the *rimenanuwe* called *toto*.

After teaching the man, the *rimenanuwe* said,

*toto* [TOH-toh]
a style of pole fishing; the fisherman drags his line in front of him left to right and back again, wiggling the line to attract fish.

*mōn* [meuhn]

233

"We'll fish together." And they caught a lot of fish in just a short amount of time.

"Now you take the fish," said the *rimenanuwe*. "I don't want any of it. Come back again tomorrow, and come at the exact same time. When the tide is just this high."

So the Ellice man took the fish and went on home. When he got back, all the people were surprised. Usually he came back with only half a basket of fish, but now he had two full baskets. They wondered how he had done that.

For three days the man did this. For three days he brought back a lot of fish. Then on the fourth day the *rimenanuwe* asked him, "Please come back again tomorrow at the same time, because I have something special I want to ask you."

The next day the *rimenanuwe* said, "I want to make you my **jera**."

*jera* [JEH-rah]
best friend

So from then on when they saw each other they called out, "*Iakwe, jera.*"

"From now on, I'd like to live with you," the *rimenanuwe* told the Ellice man. "Your island will be my island, you and I will be like family. Also, can you please find me a girlfriend?"

"That's a good idea!" said the Ellice man. "We'll do that. We'll ask all the parents here who'd like to take you as a husband."

So they went on to the first house. And the Ellice man asked if they'd like to have their daughter marry his new friend. "My friend is different from us, a *rimenanuwe*, yes, but he is just like me."

But the people at that first house said, "No way. He's like a demon. I'm not marrying my daughter to that little man." And they shut the door.

It happened at the second house they visited. And so it went from house to house, always the same. "Get away. Go away." Not even one family in Ellice wanted their daughter to marry this *rimenanuwe*.

Finally, the Ellice man got a good idea. "Don't worry, in our custom, I'll find one in my family. My sister has a daughter, and she will marry you."

Now at that same time, the chief of the island called all his people together to collect and make thatch for his new house. Everyone came together to help the chief, including the man and the *rimenanuwe*.

The *rimenanuwe* told the chief he and his new friend would bring fish for everyone, just the two of them. All the men were surprised. "You two by yourself are going to feed all these people? You're crazy."

The chief said to them, "Okay, but if you don't bring enough fish for everyone, we will kill you." The chief called to the people, "All right, everyone off to get other food; these two alone will bring the fish for us all."

Five days they all worked together to build the house. Each day the Ellice man reported what was happening to the *rimenanuwe*. The Ellice man was scared. "When are we going fishing?" he asked the *rimenanuwe*. "Tomorrow is the last day before the time, and we haven't done anything."

The *rimenanuwe* just said, "Don't worry about it. When is the feast?"

"Tomorrow morning!"

"Okay, no problem. You just go to sleep now."

But the Ellice man couldn't sleep. At midnight he visited the *rimenanuwe* and asked him again. The *rimenanuwe* told him not to worry, just rest. At two the man visited again. Don't worry, he was told by the *rimenanuwe*.

At five in the morning he went to the *rime-nanuwe*.

"What time is it now?" asked the *rimenanuwe*.

"Five!"

"It's not yet morning. Relax."

Then, when the tide was back at the same height as when the two first met, the *rimenanuwe* took the Ellice man to the water. The *rimenanuwe* had made a special magic he threw into the water. Soon the water started jumping. Then almost the entire lagoon jumped. The Ellice man realized the jumping lagoon was fish, lots and lots and lots of fish.

The Ellice man ran back into the island and told all the people to come and get their own fish, because the fish were all jumping out of the water right up onto the shore. They flew out of the water, up into the bushes, and under the trees.

He told all the people, "Go to the lagoon side, grab what you can. There are fish everywhere."

All kinds of fish were there, and all the people were so surprised by all the fish. The fish were piled high on the sand. Thousands, thousands, thousands of fish piled high.

The Ellice man and the *rimenanuwe* sat together on the sand and watched the people gather in surprise.

And now all the parents wished they had given their daughters to the little man.

So now in Ellice, the people who descended from the *rimenanuwe* stay together and marry within their own clan. Those people of Ellice are smart people, and eventually they all learned how to *toto* fish.

# EB

*An island kingdom exists under the water in the Ralik chain, a kingdom called Eb.*

*Etto im etto* . . . Long and long time past . . .

**Rilek**, a woman of Eb, took her two sons and settled on **Emmij**, an island in Ebon Atoll. Her sons, **Jaidrik** and **Jeieben**, did little work on Emmij, leaving most of it to her.

Now a time came when the islands of Ebon suffered a serious famine. The people had only wilted coconuts to eat. Jaidrik and Jeieben grew tired of eating dried-up coconut. They decided to go diving, to see what they could find.

"Maybe you can bring some back for others, too," Rilek said to them.

"If we can," answered the boys. "Just make sure you don't do any work while we're gone."

At that time people believed if a woman worked while her husband or sons went fishing, something bad might happen.

Jaidrik and Jeieben sailed off to find sea clams. When they found a spot far enough, the boys dived and dived and dived, all day they dived. They collected so many sea clams, their canoe barely stayed afloat. That's when they started to eat. They ate until the sea clams were all gone. Only then did they sail back to Emmij.

**Rilek** REE-lek

**Emmij** EM-mihj

**Jaidrik** JEYE-rihk

**Jeieben** JEYE-ben

"Did you get anything?" their mother asked when they arrived.

"We tried," they said, "but got nothing."

The next day the boys sailed off again. "Don't work," they reminded their mother.

"Bring something back for us," Rilek asked.

"If we're lucky." Jaidrik and Jeieben sailed, dived, collected more clams, and ate the day away.

When they returned that evening, Rilek asked, "Why do you take so long and then tell me you have nothing?"

"Why?" Jaidrik said.

"Because we search hard and can't find anything," Jeieben finished.

But Rilek knew it wasn't true.

The boys didn't know it but their mother was the *leroij*, the chiefess, of a kingdom under the water. She'd brought her boys here to test them. They weren't doing very well. So the next time they went out, she worked. The two boys dived and grabbed the sea clams, but the clams grabbed them right back and wouldn't let go.

When they hadn't returned by the next day, *Leroij* Rilek started crying. She cried as she visited the family next door. She cried and she chanted:

*Rimwin, rimwin,*
*komij lo ke neju Jaidrik im Jeieben?*

People of this house, people of this house, have you seen Jaidrik and Jeieben?

The people laughed at her, thinking she was playing some trick to get food from them. "You've lost your sons?" they said, as they slammed their door on her.

*Leroij* Rilek walked on to the next house, chanting and crying as she went:

> *Rimwin, rimwin,*
> *komij lo ke neju Jaidrik im Jeieben.*

> People of this house, people of this house,
> have you seen Jaidrik and Jeieben?

Those neighbors made fun of her as well, closing the door on the begging woman. And so it happened up and down the island, people laughing and closing doors.

*Leroij* Rilek then came to the very last house at the end of the island. An old couple lived there with their son. When the boy saw Rilek, he ran off to his parents. "There's a woman, crying."

"Mmmmm, do you hear your mother crying?" the old couple asked, adopting Rilek into their family on the spot.

> *Rimwin, rimwin,*
> *komij lo ke neju Jaidrik im Jeieben?*

> People of this house, people of this house,
> have you seen Jaidrik and Jeieben?

"Yes, yes," called the old couple. "Where are our sons?"

Rilek continued chanting:

> *Erro kar ura lom ura lom urra jeb jeb o*
> *boklim ekañ iar.*

The boys went to get sea clams and
never came out of the water.

"Our sons will soon be safe," the old couple said
as they turned to their own boy. "You've heard your
mother crying. Now go and find your brothers."

"Take this with you," Rilek told the boy, removing a special necklace from around her neck. "Put it
inside the mouth of the sea clam and twist it."

The boy dived into the lagoon. He saw Rilek's
two sons. They were barely alive. The boy did as
Rilek had told him. When he twisted the necklace,
the clams popped open. Rilek's sons floated to the
top of the water and came back to life.

*Leroij* Rilek announced, "Tomorrow let's all
wake up before the sun rises. I have something special to share with our new family."

The next morning they gathered outside the old
couple's home. Everyone except Rilek's sons. They
just slept on.

Rilek took the old people and their son to Eb, her
kingdom under the water. You see, *Leroij* Rilek had
faked the crying and the searching. She wanted to
find a boy who could be Eb's next *iroij*. Her own
sons had failed the test she set for them.

Eb is a magical land, where coconuts hang to the
ground. Banana, pandanus, papaya, breadfruit are
so plentiful, no one ever wants for anything.

The two old people died there. And their son
became the *iroij* of this magical island. When the
two boys finally woke up, they were alone.

# EB, THE STORY CONTINUED

*I'll tell you part two of the story of the magical kingdom under the water, the island we call Eb.*

*Etto im etto* . . . Long and long time past . . .

One year after *Leroij* Rilek took the old couple to Eb, a fisherman named **Lamil** was fishing in the lagoon of Ebon. He always fished there. He always caught a lot of fish.

**Lamil** lah-MEEL

As he was fishing on this one day, his line got caught. He pulled up, the line came loose, but his hook was gone. He saw a lot of **bwebwe**, yellowfin fish, nearby, so he dived in to find them.

***bwebwe***
BWAY-bway

As he swam about, Lamil saw the island of Eb. A bubble of fresh air floated nearby. He swam into it and came upon *Leroij* Rilek.

"Can I help you?" she asked.

"Thank you," Lamil said. "I was fishing, and one fish caught my hook. So I came down here to look for it."

Rilek told him, "Look at my house over there. Tell me if you see your hook."

Hooks covered *Leroij* Rilek's house. Big hooks and small hooks hung from the roof and walls. Beautiful, polished hooks sparkled. Rilek had collected all these hooks from the many fish that had gotten away. Lamil couldn't find his.

"What kind of fish were you trying to catch?" Rilek asked him.

"The *bwebwe*."

Rilek called to the *bwebwe*. Every last one of them swam over to the *leroij*.

"Which fish is it?" Rilek asked, as they swam by.

Soon a fish with a hook still stuck in its mouth swam near Lamil. "That one. There it is!" he told the *leroij*.

"Come," Rilek called to the fish. She gently removed the hook from the fish's jaw.

"Thank you," Lamil said. "Thank you so much for your help."

Not long after Lamil returned to Ebon, another man heard the story. He wanted to find out if this kingdom was real, if all those hooks really were down there. But he just threw his hook into the water and dived after it. He saw Eb and swam into the bubble of air.

"*Iakwe*," Rilek said. "Can I help you?"

"I was fishing for *bwebwe*," the man told her, "but one of your fish took off with my hook."

"Look at my house there," she said, "and tell me if you see your hook."

The man saw the most beautifully carved hook made from fishbone.

"That one. That one!" the man said.

"That's your hook?" asked Rilek.

The man said, "Oh yes, yes, it's mine."

"You're trying to trick me," Rilek told him, "so you will die."

And the man did.

*[Iban almost couldn't finish the story because he started laughing. "Don't be telling lies," he said, "or you will die."]*

**IBAN EDWIN**

# LOLIN

*Etto im etto* . . . Long and long time past . . .

Lolin always went fishing, like all the men of his island.

**Lolin** LAW-lihn

He was out fishing one night alone. He saw a stranger fishing just a hundred feet from him. Lolin looked to see who it was, but the stranger disappeared. The next night the stranger fished even closer. On the third night the stranger came very close and watched.

The stranger, a *noniep*, or helpful spirit, said, "Friend, the way you *toto* fish is like this." The *nonieb* showed Lolin. As they *toto* fished together, the *noniep* threw all her fish into Lolin's basket. They caught a lot of fish.

Some people of the island went to Lolin's house to visit. Lolin's wife told them, "Let's wait a bit, my husband is still out."

When Lolin's basket was full, the *noniep* said, "Tomorrow we'll catch more." They paddled off their separate ways.

Lolin returned home. The people visiting said, "**Wa-rar**, you caught a lot of fish."

**wa-rar**
[wah-RAHR]
exclamation of
frustration

Each day the *noniep* appeared to Lolin. Each day following, they caught more fish. Lolin took lots home every day.

The men of the island got suspicious. They kept asking Lolin how he got all that food.

"I just go to the end of the island," he said. The men didn't believe that, because he always came back with so much more food than any of them— more food than you can find on a tiny island.

After several days, the *noniep* told Lolin his wife would have a baby. "It won't be your wife's baby," the *noniep* said. "It'll be your and my son. But your wife will birth it."

"My wife's not pregnant," Lolin said.

"Will be soon," said the *noniep,* and she gave Lolin food and fish to make his wife and the unconceived boy healthy.

Soon after, the men decided to follow Lolin. They hid in the thicket and watched as the *noniep* appeared with so much food and so many fish.

The men were jealous. Those men stepped out of the woods, ready to collect all that food, too. The *noniep*, and the food, disappeared.

Four months later Lolin's wife gave birth to a healthy boy.

The noniep never returned.

But the people of that island, Namdrik, are the best at *toto* fishing. Lolin taught them.

# GLOSSARY AND PRONUNCIATION GUIDE

*abji* [AHB-jee] to grab

*adje* [AHD-jay] drum

**Aelōñ Kein Ad** eye-LEUHNG kayn ahr

**Aelōñlaplap** eye-LEUHNG-lap-lap

**Aeninjena** EYE-nihn-je-nah

**Ailuk** EYE-look

**Airok** EYE-ruk

*aj* [ahj] the thatch for roofs of traditionally built houses

**Ak** ahk

*akūt* (also *ekit*) [EH-kiht] to look for lice

*alap* [AH-lahp] clan heads

*anidreb* [ah-NEE-reb] a game similar to footbag

*anij* [AH-neej] a spirit

**Annung** AHN-nuhng

**Arbar** AHR-bahr

*armwe* AHRM-weh

**Arno** AHR-noh

*atat* [aht-AHT] a ground-covering plant, traditionally used to make a fine fiber; its leaves are very small.

**Aur** AH-oor

**Awon** AH-wohn

*bale* BAH-lay

*baret* BEYE-ret

**Barulep** bah-ROO-lep

*bedbed* [BED-bed] newborn coral reef

**Bejbejinna** bej-BEJ-een-nah

*bidrikdrik maroñroñ* [BIH-rihk-rihk MAH-rohng-rohng] a custom that states that if you have something, even if it's little, you should share it with other people

*bijbeto* [BIZH-be-doh] flotsam (floating wreckage)

**Bikar** bee-KAHR

**Bikien** BEEK-ee-en

**Bikon** BIH-kohn

*bilkin mā* BIHL-kihn meh

*bo* [bwo] rafters

*bōjo* [BEUH-joh] a basket

**Bok** bohk

*bōkanje* [beuh-KAHN-jeh] the tradition of traveling island to island looking for gifts for a pregnant wife

**Bōkbōk** BEUHK-beuhk

**Bokenjine** BOHK-en-jih-neh

**Bokidik** boh-KIH-drihk

**Bokilañ** BOHK-ee-lahng

**Boknake** bohk-NAH-keh

**Bolden Elbon** BOHL-den el-BOHN

*bu ball* [BOO ball] a marble game

**Bub** buhb

*bubu* [BOO-boo] magic

*bwebwenato* [bway-bway-NAH-doh] story, conversation; stories believed to be true

**Bwilbilinlokerem** bwihl-bwihl-ihn-LOH-ker-em

**Debdeb** REB-reb

*dekalal* [reh-KAY-lahl] basaltic rock; it holds heat well, through as many as fifty firings in an earth oven.

*dri-anijnij* [ree-AH-nihj-nihj] magic-worker

*dri-bubu* [ree-BOO-boo] sorcerer

*dri-bwebwenato* [ree-bway-bway-NAH-doh] storyteller

**Dridri** REE-ree

*dri-eñod* [ree-eng-OHR] fisherman

**Eb** eb

**Ebon** eh-BOHN

**Een** en

**Ejelben** eh-JEL-ben

*ejjōb aō* [EJ-jeuhb aeuh] a kind of baseball, using only hands and a Marshallese woven ball

*ejtōbtōb* [EJ-teuhb-teuhb] a custom that states that if people eat good food and don't share with others, they will remain hungry

*ekkwal* [EK-kwahl] sennit, or coconut rope

**Elibobo** eh-lee-BOH-boh

*emjak* [EM-jahk] rock anchor

**Emmij** EM-mihj

**Eniwetak** en-ee-WEH-tahk

*eọ* [EH-aw] tattoo

**Eonikje** eh-OH-nihk-jeh

**Erikub** ER-ee-koob

*etto im etto* [ET-toh ihm ET-toh] "long and long time past"

**Ewo** EH-woh

**Hecekeia Jibba** hes-eh-KAY-ee-ah JIHB-bah

*iakwe* [ee-ah-KWEH] literally, "You are the rainbow"; greetings, love

*iakwe komi* [ee-ah-KWEH keh-MEE] greetings

**Ib** ihb

**Iban Edwin** ee-BAHN ED-ween

*ie* [eeay] a large needle used to
make mats

**Ieb** yeb

*ilemej* [ee-LEH-mej] birthmark

**Inedrel** IHN-eh-rehl

*inoñ* [ih-NOHNG] stories not
believed to be true

*iroij* [ih-ROHJ] chief

**Iroñ** ee-ROHNG

*jab bo kake* [jahb boh KAH-kay]
not listening to someone

**Jabōnbok** JAH-beuhn-bohk

**Jabwor** jahb-OHR

**Jackning** JAK-neeng

**Jaidrik** JEYE-rihk

**Jajōn** jay-JEUHN

*jaki* [JAH-kee] mats

*jakmi* [JAHK-meye] cooked
coconut milk

**Jakunne** jah-KOON-nay

**Jaluit** JA-loo-iht

**Jamokro** JAH-moh-kroh

**Jang** jahng

**Janinwe** JAH-nihn-weh

*jao* [JAH-oh] birthmark

*jebwa* [JEB-wah]

**Jeh** jeh

**Jeieben** JEYE-ben

**Jejjed** JEJ-jehr

*jekajeje* [JEH-kah-jeh-jeh]
coconut milk warmed under
the sun

*jekōkōke* jeh-keuh-KEUH-keh

*jekoro* [JEH-koh-roh] fresh
coconut milk

**Jeljel Jerbal** JEL-jel jer-BAHL

**Jelkwon** JEL-kwohn

*jema* [JEH-mah] father

**Jemeluit** JEH-meh-loot

**Jemenkul** JEH-men-kool

**Jemo** JEH-moh

**Jena** JEN-ah

*jera* [JEH-rah] best friend

**Jia Hisaiah** JEE-ah heye-SAY-ee-
ah

**Jiadel** jee-AH-rehl

**Jibedbō** JEE-ber-beuh

*jidip inoñ, jidim jedu* [JIH-rihp
ih-NOHNG JIH-rihm je-DOO]
"That's the end of the story."

*jij* jihj

*jilel* [JIH-lel] conch shell

**Jimunne** jih-MUHN-nay

*jinō* [JIH-neuh] mother

**Jirabelbel** jih-RAH-bel-bel

*jirul* [jih-RUHL] small shells that look like eyes

*jitdam kapeel* [JIHT-rahm kah-PEL] the custom of always asking strangers who their relatives are and what their *joui* are

**Jobi** JOH-bee

*jojo* [JOH-joh] flying fish

**Jolukwor** JOH-luhk-woor

**Jorju Arre** JOHR-joo AHR-reh

**Josapeth Amram** JOH-sah-bet AHM-rahm

*joui* [JOH-wee] clan

*jubbub in mañ* [JOOB-boob ihn mahng] pandanus thorn

**Kaben** KAH-ben

**Kaben Meto** KAH-ben MEH-toh

**Kabōredkoj** kah-beuhr-ER-kwoj

**Kadjo** KAHR-joh

**Kaekae** KAY-kay

**Kaibad** KEYE-bahr

**Kaiju** KEYE-joo

*kajer* [kah-JEHR] a game

**Kajkaki** KAHJ-kah-kee

**Kako** [KAH-koh] A *kako* is a rooster.

**Kañal** KAHNG-ahl

*kañal* KAHNG-ahl

*karuk* [kah ROOK] a small crab

*kear* KEH-ahr

*kelok* [KEH-lohk] to fly

*kiar* [keeahr] perfume made from shark

**Kiat** KEE-aht

*kiden* [KIH-ren] a flowering tree

**Kikā** KEE-kay

*kilek* [KEE-lek] a large basket

*kilin wōt ne* [KIH-lihn weuht neh]

*kinji* [KIHN-jee] pinch

*kiō* KEE-euh

**Kiribati** [KIH rih bus] an independent island group southeast of the Marshall Islands

**Kōbelokie** keuh-beh-LOH-kee

**Koju** KOH-joo

**Kolej** koh-LEJ

*kōlkōl* [KEUHL-keuhl] an animal capable of imitating any noise

*kom emmol* [kohm em-MOHL] thank you (to several people)

*kommol tata* [KOHM-mohl DAH-dah] thank you very much

*koñal* KOHNG-ahl

*kōnat* KEUH-naht

*koñe* [KOHNG-eh] wood of the ironwood tree

*kōno* KEUH-noh

*koonwadrik* [keuhn-WAH-rihk] an old word for *iroij*, or chief

*kor* [kohr] coconut shells with a hole in the middle

*kōrkōr* [KEUHR-keuhr] small canoe

*kōtkōt* [KEUHT-keuht] a bird, the ruddy turnstone

**Kōtorlok Botoklok** keuh-TOHR-lohk BOH-tohk-lohk

**Kowak** KOH-wahk

*kubañ* koo-BAHNG

**Kumar** koo-MAHR

**Kwajalein** KWAHJ-ah-lehn

**Kweat** [KWAY-eht] A *kweat* ia an octopus or squid.

**Lade** LAH-reh

**Lae** leye

**Lajibedbō** lah-JEE-behr-beuh

**Lakilmej Line** lah-KIHL-mej leyen

**Lamare** LAH-mah-reh

**Lañelinwōd** lahng-el-IHN-weuhr

**Langmouir** LAHNG-moh-eer

**Lanij** LAH-neej

**Latoña** lah-TOHNG-ah

**Launbikar** LAWHN-bih-kahr

*lejale* [LEH-jah-leye] the *iroij*'s wife

**Lejla** LEJ-lah

**Leli** LEH-lee

**Lene Langbol** LAHNG-eh LANHG-bohl

*leroij* [LEH-rohj] chiefess

**Letao** LEH-dow

**Letujāwa** leh-TOO-jeh-wah

**Lewatonmour** le-WAH-tuhn-moh-oor

**Lewoj** LEH-wohj

**Lijebake** lee-jeh-BAH-keh

**Lijeia** lee-JEYE-ee-ah

**Lijoko** lee-JOH-koh

**Lijuwawa** lee-joo-WAH-wah

**Likāliklik** lee-KAY-lihk-lihk

**Likiep** LEE-kee-eb

**Likinmōrlik** lih-kihn-MEUHR-lihk

**Likirebjel** lee-kih-REB-jel

**Likjor** LIHK-johr

**Likukure** lee-KOO-koo-reh

*limakak* [LEE-mah-kahk] kite

**Limarien** lee-mahr-ee-EN

**Limjalulu** lihm-JAH-loo-loo

**Litakboki** lee-tahk-BOH-kee

**Lō Beibat** leuh BAY-bat

**Lō Kokelōk** leuh koh-KAY-leuhk

**Lobaia** loh-BAH-ee-ah

**Lōbetaña** leuh-bay-tah-NGA

**Lōbokwa** leuh-bohk-WAH

**Lodiren** loh-RIH-ren

**Lōiroij** leuh-ih-ROHJ

**Lojourur** loh-johr-OOR

**Lok** lohk

**Lolin** LAW-lihn

**Lōmanjideb** leuh-MAHN-jih-reb

**Lōmanjirilik** leuh-mahn-jih-REE-lihk

**Lōmanluklok** leuh-MAHN-luhk-lohk

**Lōnen** LEUH-nen

**Lōññar** LEUHNG-ngahr

**Lōrōkewa** leuh-reuh-KAY-wah

*lot* [laht] hollow coconuts

**Loto** LOH-toh

**Loujen** LOH-oo-jen

**Lowa** LOH-wah

**Lubale** loo-BAH-leh

**Lukonwor** LUH-kohn-wohr

**Luōj** luh-EUHJ

**Luwajwoj** loo-WAHJ-wojh

**Madmad** MAHR-mahr

**Majuro** MAH-joo-roh

**Makaulij** mah-KOW-lihj

**Maloelap** mah-LOH-eh-lap

*marjej* [MAHR-jehj] a weed called the "toilet paper plant"; it has almost no woody parts.

**Marmar** MAHR-mahr

*mejenkwaad* [MEH-jen-kwahr] female demon

*mejenwōd* [MEH-jen-weuhr] a large clamshell

**Mejin Jitiam** meh-JIHN JIH-tee-ahm

**Mejit** MEH-jeet

*mekwon* [MEH-kwohn] boiled and grated pandanus fruit

**Menenaluk** men-en-AH-look

*merā* meh-REYE

**Mili** MIH-leh

*mokan* [MOH-kahn] a food made from cooked and grated pandanus wrapped in a coconut leaf

**Mokba** MOHK-bah

*mōn* [meuhn]

**Monebbort** MOH-neb-bohrt

*mōnmōnbwij* [meuhn-MEUHN-bwihj] the custom of taking care of the *iroij*'s family whenever they visit *moun* [moh-OON] magic used to make men brave

*mwio* [MWEE-oh] a large fishing net made out of coconut leaf

**Nadrikdrik** NAH-rihk-rihk

**Namdrik** NAHM-rihk

**Namu** NAH-moo

**Nānākuli** [NAH NAH koo lee] a town on the Wai'anae Coast of the island of O'ahu, Hawai'i

**Narlo** NAHR-loh

**Neilem Baneb** NEH-lem bah-NEB

**Nitwa Jeik** NIHT-wah jayk

*nitwa* NIHT-wah

*no* [noh] a prickly sea creature

*noniep* [NOH-nee-ep] a helpful spirit

**Okona** oh-koh-NAH

**Okono** oh-koh-NOH

**pandanus** fiber made from the leaves of the screw pine tree; it is used in weaving mats and other items

*raj* [rahj] whales

**Ralik** REYE-lihk

**Ratak** RAH-dahk

**Raur** rah-OOR

**Relik** REE-lihk

*ribelle* [rih-BEL-leh] foreigners

**Ri-Jaluit** ree-JA-loo-iht

*rijerbal* [ree-jer-BAHL] workers

*ri-joran* [ree-joh-RAHN] a bad person

**Ri-kwoj** ree-KWOHJ

**Rile** REE-leh

**Rilek** REE-lek

*rimenanuwe* [ree-MEN-ahn-way] the legendary "little people" of the Marshall Islands, similar to the leprechauns of Ireland or the *menehune* of Hawai'i

**Ris** rihj

*rittoro* [rih-TOH-roh] people long ago

**Riwitiñtiñ** ree-WIH-ting-ting

*riwōt* [REE-weuht] a game named for a toy canoe

**Rongelap** ROHNG-eh-lahp

**Rongerik** ROHNG-eh-rihk

**Rongrong** ROHNG-rohng

**Rubin** ROO-bihn

**Tak** tahk

**Taka** TAH-kah

**Take** TAH-keh

**Tarawa** TAHR-ah-wah

**Tarkumar** TAHR-koo-mahr

**tibnol** [TIHB-ngol] a large canoe

**tilan** [tee-LAHN] pumice (porous volcanic rock)

**Tobolar** TOH-boh-lahr

**Toelae** TOH-leye

**Tolewe** TOH-le-weh

**Tonke Aisea** TOHN-keh eye-SAY-ah

**tōra** [TEUH-rah] a raft of coconuts

**toto** [TOH-toh] a style of pole fishing; the fisherman drags his line in front of him left to right and back again, wiggling the line to attract fish.

**Tutu** TOO-too

**ụ** [oo] fish trap

**Ujae** OO-jeye

**ujelā** [OO-jeh-leye] a sail

**ujelā mañ** [OO-jeh-leye mahng] a sail

**um** [oom] underground oven

**Uom** ohm

**Utrik** OO-trihk

**waini** [weye-NEE] fallen coconuts

**wallap** [WAHL-lahp] a canoe

**wa-rar** [wah-RAHR] exclamation of frustration

**Wodmej** WOHD-mej

**Woja** WOH-jah

**Wollet** WOHL-let

**Wōnbar** WUEHN-bahr

**Wōt Kileplep** WEUHT kih-LEP-lep

**Wotje** WOHT-jeh

**wut ilomar** [WOOT ee-loh-MAHR] a shrub and tree with very large, round leaves used to cover food